1968

This book may be kept

*Foundations of Euclidean
and Non-Euclidean Geometry*

Foundations
of Euclidean
and Non-Euclidean
Geometry

Ellery B. Golos

Ohio University

HOLT, RINEHART and WINSTON INC.
New York · Chicago · San Francisco · Atlanta · Dallas
Montreal · Toronto · London

To LILA

Preface

This book is an attempt to present, at an elementary level, an approach to geometry in keeping with the spirit of Euclid, and in keeping with the modern developments in axiomatic mathematics. It is not a comprehensive study of Euclidean geometry—far from it; it is not a survey of various types of geometry. And while it is designed to meet prerequisites in geometry for secondary school teachers, it is neither a review of high-school topics, nor an extension of such topics, as has been customarily covered over the years in books designed for college geometry.

The emphasis of the book is on the method of presentation rather than on presenting a mass of information. It is in the spirit of Euclid in two senses: it is a synthetic approach to geometry; it is an axiomatic approach.

The author recognizes the fact that, in high schools, there are many advantages to developing geometry by the method now coming into use. We refer to the method credited to Birkhoff and Beatley, and adopted and modified by the School Mathematics Study Group. It is, at this time, the simplest and most practical way to present the subject matter at that level. However, there is much to be said for presenting the college mathematics major and prospective teacher with a different approach. It is hoped that this book will serve this purpose.

The book attempts to blend several aspects of mathematical thought: namely, intuition, creative thinking, abstraction, rigorous deduction, and the excitement of discovery. It is designed to do so at an elementary level. In covering these aspects, it falls rather naturally into three parts.

The first part is designed to give the student the tools, insight, and motivation to approach elementary geometry from a new perspective and with an open mind. While portions of this part of the book may seem a bit too abstract for the beginner, the author has found that there are enough concrete interpretations to keep most students on a firm footing, and enough new challenges to stimulate them.

The second part is meant to introduce the student to a modern, rigorous approach to the foundations of geometry. It attempts to introduce and pursue many important topics that are often slighted; at the same time, it does not, as is so often the case in studies in foundations, introduce an axiom system which is so delicately pure that it seems never to arrive at the standard theorems of elementary geometry. Thus it combines both rigor and intuition.

The third part is devoted to non-Euclidean geometry, and as such, forces the student to reason without placing too much reliance on his intuition. It is to be hoped that the first two parts have prepared him for this.

It is best, perhaps, to attempt to devote at least two academic quarters to the book. We have found, in several years of teaching this material, that it can be covered in one semester if, instead of lecturing, the instructor uses class time in clarifying and answering questions about content and "problems." This technique is not merely a time-saving device. It forces the student to read; it stimulates class discussion; it sometimes even leads to "discovering" new truths. Because we have used this approach, we have attempted to make the text self-contained and readable.

The partitioning of the text offers a greater degree of flexibility in its use. Part II can be used by itself (perhaps with some of Part I as outside reading). Other possibilities are to use Parts I and II; Parts II and III (Chapter 4 as outside reading). The time one spends on each part will depend greatly upon the time one wishes to devote to proofs and exercises; they should not be slighted, because they enrich the course considerably.

Because the emphasis throughout the text is on its approach to the material rather than on its specific content, and because the text is available to students at an elementary level, it has been our experience that it has a great deal of "transfer" value. We have found this to hold both in preparing the student for the next geometry course, and in just giving him an edge in gaining that nebulous goal called "mathematical maturity."

But even if the text achieves none of the foregoing, the author will be pleased if it stimulates any reader to pursue one of the topics on his own.

The author wishes to express his appreciation to the Cambridge University Press for giving him permission to quote from its definitive publication on Euclid: *The Thirteen Books of Euclid's Elements*, by T. L. Heath. The proofs of several theorems are reproduced in their entirety within the text; and statements of the axioms, definitions, and theorems of *Book I* are quoted in the text and listed in the Appendix.

If there are any errors in the book, they are present in spite of the many helpful suggestions and constructive criticisms made by colleagues and friends who read and used a preliminary version of the work. The author wishes especially to thank Professor W. T. Fishback, who first encouraged him to write the book and used a preliminary manuscript at Earlham College; Robert Lifsey, who used the same version of the manuscript at Ohio University; Professor V. Klee, who, as an editorial consultant for Holt, Rinehart and Winston, offered many constructive suggestions along with comments which inspired the author to try harder to achieve his aims; and finally, the author wishes to express his gratitude to E. D. Goodrich, who, with painstaking care, has read all of the versions through which the manuscript evolved.

Thanks are also due to Paula Smith, who did such a fine job of typing the final manuscript.

E. B. G.

Athens, Ohio
February 1968

Contents

part 1

An Analysis
of Axiomatic Systems

introduction

Geometry, as we shall study it in this volume, has undergone a long history of evolution. The greatest change has been in the approach to the subject matter, in the techniques of proof, rather than in the subject matter itself. The first, perhaps the most drastic such change, occurred more than two thousand years ago.

The ancient Egyptians knew geometry well, if by geometry one means certain properties and relations that figures have with themselves and with each other. They knew, for example, that if they formed a

1

triangle of sides 3, 4, and 5 units long, it would be a right triangle; they undoubtedly used this and many other geometric facts to survey their lands—a practice necessitated by the yearly flooding of the Nile—and to construct the awe-inspiring pyramids that still stand today. But there is no evidence that they could generalize this fact to such a statement as "any triangle such that the sum of the squares on two sides is equal to the square on the third side must be a right triangle." And even if they could make such a generalization they would not have been able to prove it, for the very idea of having to "prove" a statement would have been foreign to them.

It was the Greeks who first introduced the idea of "proofs." The Pythagoreans, with their fascination for numbers, gave great impetus to the investigation of mathematics for its own sake. Many minds delved into the problems of geometry and contributed to the discovery of new facts, facts that somehow needed tying together. It took the genius of Euclid, who created the Elements around the year 300 B.C., to achieve this synthesis. It should not detract at all from Euclid's genius to acknowledge that his work is in large part a compilation of the works of his predecessors, for it is the manner in which the work is organized rather than its particular content that has made it one of the most influential works ever produced.

Without the high praise, the same point might be made about the organization of this book. The average reader will undoubtedly find some of the content familiar; he can be assured that much of the rest occurs elsewhere in the literature of mathematics. It is hoped, however, that the book's organization will be not merely different but instructive.

We shall attempt to explain and motivate the particular organization of this text so that the reader will be in position to approach it with our over-all objective in mind. We shall first give a brief and selective review of the history of the subject from the time of Euclid.

History

From a few basic assumptions, and a few definitions, Euclid proceeded to prove more than 400 theorems. These are separated into thirteen books, not all of which are concerned solely with geometry. The ordering of the theorems was so meticulously logical, proceeding step by step, theorem by theorem, from simple statements to more complex ones in so lucid and reasonable a way that the *Elements* has been used ever since as a model for such reasoning, called deductive reasoning.

One might almost hear him arguing at the Platonic academy:

So you do not believe that the sum of the angles of a triangle is equal to two right angles? Tell me, do you believe that if a side be produced, the angle formed is equal to the sum of the opposite interior angles? No? Well, then, we have but one recourse. Now surely you believe, for it is beyond doubt, that between two points a straight line may be drawn; and surely you must admit that a straight line may be extended indefinitely in either direction; and without question all right angles are equal to each other and a circle may be drawn with given radius . . . surely you admit these things, do you not? Very good, let us start with those; now then . . .

Although the *Elements* was not meant, and in many ways is not suited, for study by the very young, it came to be used as a textbook and, it has been said, went through more editions than any book except the *Bible*. It was used in both high schools and colleges until about the turn of the twentieth century; it may still be for that matter, but its unsuitability as a textbook finally overcame long tradition and it was discarded. Into its place came chaos.

The texts adopted by the high schools were generally hodgepodge collections of the material in about six of the books of the *Elements*. They covered, in some fashion or another, the material about triangles, parallelograms, area relations, circles, constructions, similarity, and solid geometry. The colleges adopted, and in many cases are still using, texts incorporating "advanced" Euclidean theorems and perhaps a sampling of topics from other geometries. But seldom was there an attempt to preserve the order of the *Elements;* the very concept that made the original work a model of deductive thought for two thousand years was so altered that, while proofs were still presented, the basic idea of an axiomatic approach to the subject matter disappeared.

To a large extent, this came about through necessity, not mere caprice. Over the centuries it came to be recognized that the *Elements* contains many flaws—we shall discuss these later. Attempts to correct them were made through the ages, but such attempts were basically piecemeal and were therefore destined to fail in a work of such coherence. In a different era, perhaps, tradition would have won out, but the late nineteenth century was a period of intensive questioning and critical self-analysis in mathematics. New standards of rigor and precision arose, and a work so flawed had little place—hallowed as that place might be.

Contributing much to this critical analysis of the foundations of mathematics, and to the demise of the sanctity of the *Elements*, was the discovery in the mid-nineteenth century of non-Euclidean geometries. Euclid's geometry, which before this time had been regarded not simply as a mathematical system but as a description of the space-world around us, came to be regarded as merely another consistent geometry with no special claims to the truth. The effect this had on the status of axioms, and the resultant effect on the approach to geometrical systems, will be discussed later in some detail. For now, we are content merely to point out a historical irony: the non-Euclidean geometries, and the near extinction of the *Elements*, grew out of attempts to improve the *Elements*, from a long history of trying to prove that one of Euclid's axioms—the Parallel Postulate, or, the Fifth—was really a theorem. Unfortunately, the technical apparatus for constructing proofs in the new geometries was almost entirely an adaptation of that used in Euclidean geometry. The new geometry was thus open to the same criticisms as those directed at the original.

It was not until the turn of this century that the great German mathematician David Hilbert (1862–1943) set forth a system of axioms from which Euclidean geometry would follow with all the rigor demanded by the twentieth century. He corrected the errors of commission and omission that abounded in the *Elements* but, in doing so, left the axiomatic approach to geometry unsuited to high school use. Hilbert's system gained little popularity, moreover, in the colleges. This explains why the schools adopted the hodgepodge collections previously mentioned. Euclid's comment to a ruling monarch of his day who complained about the difficulty of the axiomatic approach to geometry still held true: there is no royal road to geometry.

While there may be no royal road, there is an easier one. Most of the errors in the *Elements* can be corrected by the simple expedient of introducing the real number system. This was first done for the high school level in the 1940's in *Basic Geometry* by Birkhoff and Beatley. More recently, the method has been adopted by the School Mathematics Study Group and is employed now in many high school textbooks. This method, aside from being a rigorous way to present geometry, has added advantages: it requires the student to use the algebra he has studied the year before; it is more readily adaptable to the study of applications of geometry; and, even more ideal for the student, it is easier. The reader, by now, is no doubt sorry to hear that this road is not to be followed here.

Objectives

While Hilbert's system may not have caught on as a method for teaching geometry, it is no exaggeration to say that his *Foundations of Geometry*, the little work in which he first presented his system, has profoundly influenced the direction and structure of a large part of twentieth century mathematics. It is a research work and sourcebook for ideas, not a textbook. In it he merely suggests a system to correct the shortcomings of

Euclid's work; but he then goes on to discuss such topics as consistency, independence, and completeness of the axioms presented. In his discussion of the independence of the various axioms, he creates the strange offshoots of a system that are discovered only when one begins to alter and change axioms. In this sense Hilbert's work is an embodiment of the spirit of twentieth century mathematics; strangely, it also expresses the spirit of Euclid. With what better reasons can one argue that it is important for the teacher of mathematics, as well as the prospective mathematics major, to be introduced to geometry from Hilbert's standpoint?

In order to understand the changes and novelties of the Hilbert system, we shall (in Chapters 1 and 4) review the *Elements*. Perhaps "review" is the wrong word, since many readers will find the presentation different from standard high school texts and from anything they have experienced previously. Surprisingly, one might even discover that it is a fascinating work, certainly one to which it is worth being introduced. Our brief introduction will consider only the first twenty-eight theorems of *Book I* of the *Elements*. Our reason for this particular selection will soon become apparent.

After impressing upon the reader the need for changes in the *Elements*, we shall (in Chapter 5) introduce, in a modified form, the Hilbert system, and proceed to develop enough material to prove some of the first twenty-eight theorems of Euclid. It should be enlightening to see how much beyond Euclid we will have to go in order to prove even these theorems with anything approaching modern rigor. It should also be enlightening to see how many theorems one can prove without introducing such concepts as continuity of lines or the infinity of points on a line. And, finally, it should be enlightening to see how we can prove some of these standard theorems of Euclidean geometry without introducing the Parallel Postulate (axiom) or anything equivalent to it. This will be necessary because we shall want to use these theorems in our development of non-Euclidean geometry.

Our study of non-Euclidean geometry (starting in Chapter 9) will differ from Euclidean geometry solely in that we contradict the Parallel Postulate and redefine *parallel*. Otherwise, the axioms and definitions we employ will be the same, and any theorem proved from these axioms will therefore hold true in the new geometry as long as no use has been made of the Parallel Postulate. Our development of the Hilbert system will be used, therefore, to develop non-Euclidean geometry with a degree of accuracy equal to that in which Euclidean geometry is presented. By this time it is to be hoped that the reader will be in a position to prove theorems from the axioms and definitions without relying too heavily on such aids as diagrams. He will know that diagrams can be dangerous if used as a part of the proof and will find that in the new geometry they can be completely misleading.

In order to appreciate fully the significance of this development from a twentieth century vantage point, we shall begin the book (Chapters 1 through 3) by discussing some modern terminology, conventions, concepts, and procedures. Also, by presenting and discussing miniature geometries that display some of the characteristics and problems common to any mathematical axiomatic system, and to Euclidean and non-Euclidean geometries in particular, we shall be giving the reader a preview of what is to come.

1 Ingredients and Tools

1.1 Definitions and Undefinitions

Richness in literary expression depends in part upon the variety of meanings that words have, upon the vagueness and ambiguities of the ideas expressed. This cannot be allowed in mathematics, where clarity and precision of expression rather than richness is needed. In mathematics, words must be carefully defined in such a way that the definitions satisfy certain prescribed criteria: simplicity; noncircularity; unique characterization. This is not always achieved, but it should at least be an ideal at which to aim. Consider the following illustration.

Let us define a "pencil" as "a sharp tool used for writing." This satisfies the criterion of simplicity, which means that any definition should use ideas and words that are as simple or simpler than the idea or words being defined. To anyone who does not know what a pencil is, the following definition would be incomprehensible: "a cylindrical instrument tapering to a conical point—as employed by an amanuensis." A definition using words more complicated than the one being defined is not of much use.

But even in a definition using simple words there is an inherent problem closely connected with the criterion of noncircularity. It is simply not possible to define every word without getting trapped either in an infinite process of defining or in circularity. Dictionary definitions are basically circular. In the suggested definition of "pencil," if one does not know the meaning of "tool" one might look it up to find it is an "instrument" or "utensil." And since it is not likely that anyone looking up the word "tool" would know the meaning of "instrument" or "utensil" either, these words would have to be looked up also. Sooner or later, a word in this chain would be defined as a "tool."

To see how serious this problem might be, consider what would happen if you wanted to use a dictionary in a foreign language, knew nothing of the foreign language, and had available only a dictionary written totally in that language. An immigrant to our shores, for example, would find any standard English language dictionary useless to him if he knew absolutely no English.

To avoid this problem it is necessary to choose some words as primitive, or undefined words, words in terms of which all the other words of the system may be defined.

So, the definition of "pencil" as a "sharp tool used for writing" satisfies the criterion of simplicity but fails to comply with noncircularity. It also fails to satisfy the third criterion, and this proves most often troublesome in mathematics.

When it is said that a suggested definition does not uniquely characterize that which is being defined—in this case a pencil—this means that it is equally applicable to other things—in this case to pens, or for that matter to quills.

To sum up, any good definition must be expressed simply, must be noncircular and must uniquely characterize that which is being defined.

With this in mind let us look at the first three definitions in Euclid's *Elements:*

1. A *point* is that which has no part.
2. A *line* is length without breadth.
3. A *straight line* is that which lies evenly with the points on itself.

These are not good definitions. The first two do not characterize that which is being defined. The first definition might as well say that *courage* is that which has no part; it might say that a *ghost* is that which has no part (or, for that matter, is length without breadth). For centuries commentators, both critics and defenders of Euclid, have discussed and argued about his definitions. Proclus (fifth century A.D.), perhaps his best commentator and defender, says, "like the *now* in time and the *unit* in number, a point is that which has no part, but in the subject matter of geometry, a point is the only thing which has no part." He thus argues that within the context this definition uniquely characterizes what is being defined. It might be argued without end whether or not these two are good definitions, but in the case of the third definition the problem is rather cut-and-dried. It is circular and should be avoided. It is impossible to define "lies evenly" without using the concept of "straight" or something synonymous with it.

In addition to the foregoing, the first two definitions have been criticized for surreptitiously introducing philosophical and physical problems that do not belong to geometry as an abstract formulation. This criticism is consistent with the spirit of Euclid, who would frown upon his work as a "practical" science. In fact, some over-enthusiastic defenders of Euclid claim that Euclid did not mean statements (1) and (2) to be definitions but was merely pointing out the abstract, nonspatial characteristics of his work. If so, if he does not mean to define point and line, he is in this respect a modern.

In modern systems the problem of circularity, as well as the problem just mentioned, is avoided by taking many words as undefined. Among these, two types are distinguished.

The *technical* terms. These vary from subject matter to subject matter. In geometry, such words as "point," "line," "congruent," "between," might be considered as the primitive or undefined terms of the system being considered. It is possible that some other system of geometry might choose other undefined terms, but those that are more or less specific to geometry are the technical terms.

The *logical, language,* or *universal* terms. These are words such as "all," "every," "any," "there exists," "at least one," "at most one," "only," "the," "although," and so on. The list goes on indefinitely, but those mentioned are the words that occur most frequently in mathematics. When a system is devised for geometry, such words as "one" and "two" are usually taken as part of the universal language.

The technical and universal terms listed in the preceding paragraphs are those which remain *undefined.* There are also technical and universal terms which are *defined;* in mathematics, definitions are usually limited to technical terms. It may surprise many readers to hear that definitions are not really necessary. This is indeed so, but we would be very verbose and would be more likely to be inaccurate and even contradictory without them. If the very same words are going to be used to describe a concept every time it is expressed, it may as well be abbreviated; that is all a definition is. If, on the other hand, the same words are not going to be used to express a concept each time it occurs, the chance for introducing contradictions increases.

The reason that mathematics leans so heavily on symbolism as a means of expressing a concept is not merely that it is a convenient shorthand, but also because it allows the mathematician to avoid expressing the same concept in words. Ordinary language words are used very sloppily, and this is true even when a mathematician uses them. As an example, consider the word "circumference" used in reference to a circle; the commonly accepted definition today is that it is the *distance* around the circle, yet one often reads and hears the word used as if it meant the circle itself, as when we speak of "a line cutting the circumference." Another phrase which frequently occurs is "the area of a circle." Yet the commonly accepted definition of a circle is: the set (or locus) of points in a plane equidistant from a fixed point called the center. Obviously, a locus of points has no area. And if by a "circle" one were to mean that portion of the plane enclosed by the locus of points, it would then be false to say that a line may cross a circle in at most two points, or that two circles can cross in at most two points, for they might have an infinite number of points in common.

Our use of symbolism will be limited. We will introduce it when convenient and avoid it when we think it best. Instead, we shall introduce many, many definitions, attempting always to satisfy the three stated criteria and to use the words precisely as they are defined. In the case of undefined technical words, the axioms of the system will restrict how they will be used.

EXERCISES 1.1

1. Compare the use of " $=$ " in the following four cases and explain any differences.

(a) $\cos^2 x + \sin^2 x = 1$

(b) $\frac{1}{2} = \frac{2}{4}$

(c) $2x + 5 = 11$

(d) angle A = angle B

2. In a beginning calculus class, the instructor has covered the blackboard with a "delta-epsilon" proof for the uniqueness of limits. When he finishes, a student asks him "If the $\lim f(x)_{x \to a} = A$ and the $\lim f(x)_{x \to a} = B$, and if things equal to the same thing are equal to each other, is it not possible to say simply that $A = B$? Why cover the board with all that stuff?"

Does the student have a point? Explain.

3. An example of a good definition is: A square is a four-sided figure bounded by straight lines; its opposite sides are parallel; and all four of its sides are equal. Answer true or false and explain your answer.

1.2 Axioms

What precisely is an axiom? One might think that this is a good place to start with a "simple, noncircular and uniquely characterizing" definition. If one is going to speak about axioms, why not immediately define what the word means? Unfortunately, it is not that easy.

Suppose we use the dictionary definition: an *axiom* is a self-evident or universally recognized truth, accepted without proof. The trouble with this is that modern mathematics would not accept this as a definition. The last part "accepted without proof" is all right, but the rest is not. To appreciate what has brought about this situation, let us look at the statements that Euclid chose as axioms.[1]

1. That a straight line may be drawn from any one point to any other point.
2. That any finite straight line may be produced to any length in a straight line.
3. That a circle may be constructed with any center, at any distance from that center.
4. That all right angles are equal to one another.
5. That, if a straight line falling on two straight lines makes the two interior angles on the same side of it taken together less than two right angles, the two straight lines, if produced indefinitely, meet on that side on which are the angles less than two right angles.

While Euclid *may* have regarded points and lines as mere abstractions, as ideals of reality that can only be approximated in our spatial world, it is unlikely that he regarded his "points" and "lines" as mere variables or undefined terms. His "points" and "lines" were in some way related to what is drawn on paper and the blackboard. His axioms were regarded as truths of the world we live in, not "mere" assumptions of someone's fancy.

As late as the eighteenth century, the great German philosopher, Immanuel Kant, built a tremendous philosophical structure around statements he called "apriori synthetic," statements, he said, such as those in geometry, which, while rooted in experience, are yet truths of an unquestionable nature.

The axioms of geometry were for two thousand years regarded as "self-evident universal truths." Is it any surprise, then, that it was not until the nineteenth century that even the possibility of a non-Euclidean geometry was put forth? Is it any surprise that Karl Friedrich Gauss (1777–1855), after developing and proving many of the theorems of a "new" geometry, kept his discoveries secret for over thirty years in fear that their revelation might harm his reputation as a mathematician? For

[1] All quotations from Euclid come from *The Thirteen Books of Euclid's Elements* translated with introduction and commentary by Sir Thomas L. Heath, 2d ed. (New York: Cambridge University Press, 1926. Reprinted by Dover Publications, Inc., 1956.)

if Euclid's geometry was the true geometry, any other would be either nonsensical or false.

Today, with the discovery and acceptance of various consistent non-Euclidean geometries, the status of axioms has undergone a radical change. To see just how drastic the change has been, contrast the views of Kant with those of Bertrand Russell (1872———). "Mathematics," Russell has said, "is that subject in which we do not know what we are talking about, or whether what we are saying is true." Even those who do not agree with such a view will recognize that it serves to emphasize an important aspect of the structure of mathematics; namely, that mathematics, instead of being the absolute science, is really the science of "if . . . then . . .". But that a statement such as Russell's can be made seriously needs explanation.

Although the way in which mathematicians regard statements has evolved over a number of years and has been influenced by many minds, Hilbert, because of the great respect he commands, has profoundly affected the course of mathematics in the twentieth century. Two of the concepts he incorporated into his axiom system for Euclidean geometry must be noted: some terms must be taken as undefined; axioms are mere assumptions about these terms.

From this beginning it is not a big step to believing that, at least where mathematics itself is concerned, the truth or falsity of the axioms is not a crucial question. For mathematics the crucial problem becomes one of "if . . . then . . ."; that is, *if* we assume such and such axioms, *then*, what follows from them. Furthermore, strictly speaking, if we regard the technical terms as undefined terms, as mere variables, then the axioms are themselves in a sense variable, or "open," sentences. As such, they cannot be said to be either true or false.

If one says, "He was the greatest mathematician who ever lived," one is not really making a *statement*—that is, to such a collection of words the labels "true" and "false" do not apply. If the sentence is changed to "Beethoven was the greatest mathematician who ever lived" or "Gauss was the greatest mathematician who ever lived," then the sentence becomes a *statement*, a collection of words to which the labels "true" or "false" may be applied. A similar comment can be made for such sentences as, "x is a whole number," "every dabba is a set of abbas." It is because of this quality of the "open" sentence that a statement such as Russell's can seriously be made.

When one begins to view axioms in this way, a question naturally arises. Of the infinite variety of such statements, how does one determine which should be used for axioms? There is no technique, no mechanical process, to help us. Assuming that one is not going to put together a meaningless, or random, collection of statements, assuming that there is some underlying unifying concept and some set of statements that one wishes to prove, the determination of the precise set to be chosen as axioms is a creative act. Yet this is only the beginning. One must then determine whether or not these axioms satisfy certain properties among themselves, and what the relationship between them and other statements, called "theorems," is. We will consider these and other questions in the next two chapters.

EXERCISES 1.2

State whether the following are true or false. Justify your answer.

1. In an axiomatic system, *every* word must be carefully defined.
2. In an axiomatic system, some *technical* words *must* be defined.
3. In an axiomatic system, if some words are defined, some must remain undefined.
4. In modern mathematics the trend is to regard axioms as self-evident truths.
5. If we regard an axiom as an open sentence, it is neither true nor false.

1.3 Logic

From a few definitions, and a few axioms, Euclid derived many "theorems"—statements which are said to "follow" from the others. Although Euclid's axioms and theorems may not be of the "if . . . then . . ." form, most of them can be put into that form. Furthermore, even if some of the statements cannot be so rephrased, the overall "if . . . then . . ." quality of the system remains. For he is saying that *if* such and such statements are granted, *then* such and such statements follow. This process of reaching conclusions from axioms is called *deduction*. The relationship that holds between the statements taken as axioms and those which are deduced from them is called *implication*. We say that the axioms *imply* the theorems.

When we consider *statements* of the form "if . . . then . . .", usually called conditional statements, we shall, contrary to common procedure, refrain from using "implies." In this context, its use tends to be confusing, because a conditional statement is just that, a statement. Given a statement P, and another statement Q, then we can define a new statement as follows:

P	Q	P → Q
T	T	T
T	F	F
F	T	?
F	F	?

P	Q	P → Q
T	T	T
T	F	F
F	T	T
F	F	T

(a)   (b)

It is customary to take Table (b) as the *definition* of "→", which can be read "arrow." Thus we might read "$P \to Q$" as "P arrow Q." More often, however, it is read as "If P then Q," which helps explain why Table (b) is chosen as its definition. Consider the following typical conditional statement: If L is a line, then there exists a point not on L. This statement says something about the existence of points under the hypothesis that L is a line; it says nothing about the existence (or nonexistence) of points if L is not a line. Looked at another way, we could say that such a statement is false under exactly one set of circumstances: L is a line, and there exists no point not on L. Ordinarily then, if L were not a line, we would say that the rest of the statement simply would not arise; that is, there is no restraint upon Q when P is false.

This is compatible with Table (a). The reason for choosing Table (b) is that logic depends on two classical laws: *The Law of Contradiction*—no statement can be both true and false and *The Law of Excluded Middle*— any statement must be either true or false.

As can be seen in Table (b), there are four possible truth combinations of P and Q. If "$P \to Q$" is to depend upon the truth of the component statements, it must have a value of either true or false in the last two lines, and because we are attempting to define a conditional statement which can be false only in the case of line two, we give the last two lines values of "T".

If we now read "$P \to Q$" as "P implies Q", which is often done in mathematics, and still interpret P implies Q to mean "Q follows from P," we can get all kinds of strange statements such as "'5 + 5 = 11' implies, 'The moon is made of spaghetti sauce.'" And who, other than a "brainwashed" student, would admit that "the moon is made of spaghetti sauce" *follows from* "5 + 5 = 11"?

Another reason for restricting our use of "implies" is that the relationship between axioms and theorems is just that, a *relation*, whereas "→" is not a relation but a type of *operation*. Thus, "→" forms a new statement, whereas "implies" does not; it "talks about" statements. Analogous to this is the difference between the "addition" operation and the "less than" relation. When two numbers are added, a new number is obtained, but when we say "2 is less than 3" we do not obtain a new number; we are expressing a relation, we are "talking about" numbers.

There are good reasons why these two concepts have tended to fuse. One is that both "→" and "implies" are read in English as "if . . . then . . .". Closely connected with this is the fact that both have similar relations with the truth values of the statements involved. Just as "→" is false when P is true and Q is false, so, if P implies Q, then one combination of truth values is ruled out; it is impossible for a true statement to imply a false statement. We wish to avoid saying, however, that *any* false statement *implies* any statement.

To sum up: we shall consider *conditional statements* as defined by Table (b). We shall consider the *relation implies* to be an undefined relation of our universal language, and shall resort to citing many, many illustrations to indicate what we mean when we say that one statement "follows" from another.

Two other operations must be introduced in this section: "not" and "and."

If "P" is a statement, "not-P" is its denial as defined by Table (c).

If "P" and "Q" are statements, then "P and Q" is the simple conjunction as defined by Table (d).

P	not-P
T	F
F	T

(c)

P	Q	P and Q
T	T	T
T	F	F
F	T	F
F	F	F

(d)

P	Q	not-Q	P and not-Q
T	T	F	F
T	F	T	T
F	T	F	F
F	F	T	F

(e)

The definitions of "→", "not" and "and" can now be used to construct new statements and their denials. For example, "*P* and not-*Q*" is the denial of "*P* → *Q*", as shown in Table (e).

It can be seen that Table (e) has *F* and *T* exactly interchanged with Table (b), and hence is its denial as defined by Table (c).

This use of "denial"—that given two statements, if one is true the other is false and if one is false the other is true, is called *contradiction*. The two statements are said to be *contradictory*. A statement such as "*P* and not-*P*" is said to be a *self-contradiction*. Whenever we want the contradiction of a statement we shall ask for *the* denial.

There is another combination that is *a* denial but not the contradiction. To illustrate, consider the statement "Today is Tuesday." A denial of this might be "Today is Wednesday." These statements deny each other but do not contradict each other, for they may both be false. Such denials are called *contraries;* they are statements that cannot both be true but that may both be false.

Associated with the conditional statement are two others worthy of specific mention: Given "If *P* then *Q*"

1. "If *Q* then *P*" is called the *converse*.
2. "If not-*Q* then not-*P*" is called the *contrapositive*.

We shall also make statements of the form "*P* if and only if *Q*," abbreviated "*P* iff *Q*," which is to be the same as the conjunction of a conditional statement and its converse. *All definitions, whether explicitly given as such or not, may be regarded as "iff" statements.*

Rather than attempt to condense a short course in logic into a brief section, we have discussed only those topics that will be required later and whose discussion within the text would have been too much of a digression. A few others will be discussed as they arise: partial converses; universal statements and their denials; and proofs, indirect and direct.

EXERCISES 1.3

1. Show that $Q \to P$ has the same truth table as not-$P \to$ not-Q.
2. Construct truth tables for: (a) $P \to Q$ (b) $P \to$ not-Q (c) P and Q (d) P and not-Q and compare.

Are $P \to Q$ and $P \to$ not-Q contradictory? Are any of the statements above contradictory to each other?

3. Write the converse of not-$Q \to$ not-P.
4. Write the contrapositive of not-$P \to Q$.
5. Write the converse and contrapositive of each of the following.

(a) If two lines are parallel, they have no point in common.

(b) If two angles are congruent, they are right angles.

(c) If a triangle has three equal angles, it is equiangular.

6. Is the converse of every definition, expressed in "if . . . then . . ." form, true? Explain.

7. Is the converse of every true conditional statement a true statement? Explain.

8. Is the converse of every false conditional statement a false conditional statement? Explain.

9. (a) Does "P only if Q" mean "$P \to Q$" or "$Q \to P$"?

   (b) Does "P if Q" mean "$P \to Q$" or "$Q \to P$"?

10. Write in "if . . . then . . ." form:

(a) Two lines are parallel only if they have no point in common.

(b) Two lines are parallel if they have no point in common.

11. Separate into two statements of the "if . . . then . . ." form:

(a) Two sides of a triangle are congruent iff the angles opposite them are congruent.

(b) Two lines are perpendicular to a third line iff they are parallel.

(c) Two lines, intersected by a third, are parallel iff the alternate interior angles are congruent.

1.4 Sets

The concept of a *set* shall also remain undefined. When we say that a set is any collection of objects we are not defining it. We could just as easily use the words *collection, class,* or *group.* But the word *set* is customary in mathematics, while the word *class* is used in philosophy, and no mathematician would use the word *group,* which has another special meaning. The modern mathematical theory of sets is usually credited to the German mathematician, Georg Cantor, who, in attempting to define the word "set," became involved with an intricate problem. It is because of this that mathematicians no longer attempt to define the word.

There is a standard notational shorthand that goes with the theory of sets. We shall for the most part avoid its use in this book but, because it is a common and convenient timesaving device in classroom lectures, we shall introduce the basic concepts and symbols of set theory.

If a set, denoted by S, is a collection of things, say a, b, and c, it is written:

$$S = \{a, b, c\}$$

Two sets are said to be *equal* iff they have the same elements. Thus, the set $A = \{a\}$ and the set $B = \{a, a, a, a\}$ are to be regarded as the same set. Two sets which are not equal are said to be *distinct*.

To say that a *belongs to* S, or *is an element* of S, one writes:

$$a \in S$$

To deny this, one writes:

$$a \notin S$$

If A is any set such that all of its elements are also elements of S, then one says that A is *a subset of* S. From the example S given before, if $A = \{a, b\}$ then A is a subset of S, which is written:

$$A \subseteq S$$

By definition, it follows that $A \subseteq A$, and $S \subseteq S$, or, any set has itself as a subset. If one wishes to write that A is a subset of S but not equal to S, this can be written:

$$A \subset S$$

and read "A is a *proper subset* of S." Many authors use this symbol for subset and have no symbol for proper subset.

If one wishes to talk about all the elements of a set, one might merely list them. But suppose that this cannot be done. Then the following notation is useful:

$$S = \{x | x \text{ is a point}\}$$

which is read "the set of all x such that x is a point" or more naturally "the set of all points."

If A and B are sets, then the elements common to both sets, that is, the set of elements which belong to both A and B, is called the *intersection*. To denote this, we use the notation:

$$A \cap B$$

It may happen that two sets have no elements in common; in such a case the sets are called *disjoint*, symbolized by:

$$A \cap B = \phi$$

where ϕ is called the *null*, or *empty* set, *the* set that has no elements. From the definition of subset, it follows that the null set is a subset of any set.

Because in this book we are going to be considering lines as sets of points, we shall adopt the following convention. Whenever we use the verb "intersects" we shall mean a nonempty intersection. So we shall never say that two sets intersect when in fact they are disjoint.

If A and B are sets, then the set of all elements that belong either to A, or to B, or to both, is called the *union*. This is denoted by:

$$A \cup B$$

For example, if $A = \{a, b, c\}$ and $B = \{a, b, d\}$ then $A \cup B = \{a, b, c, d\}$. Observe that there is no need to write $A \cup B = \{a, a, b, b, c, d\}$.

Further comments on this topic will be incorporated into the text.

EXERCISES 1.4

1. If $S = \{1, 2, 3, 4, 5, 6\}$ $L = \{1, 3, 5\}$ $M = \{2, 4, 6\}$ $N = \{4, 6\}$ $P = \{6\}$, find:

(a) $L \cup M$

(b) $L \cap M$

(c) $N \cap N$

(d) $M \cup M$

(e) $L \cap P$

(f) List all the subsets of N; of M.

2. Using L, M, N of exercise 1, which of the following hold?

(a) $L \cup (M \cap N) = (L \cup M) \cap (L \cup N)$

(b) $L \cap (M \cup N) = (L \cap M) \cup (L \cap N)$

(c) $L \cup (M \cap N) = (L \cup M) \cap N$

(d) $L \cap (M \cup N) = (L \cap M) \cup N$

3. If $X \cup Y = X$ and $X \cap Y = X$, then $X = Y$. True or false. Explain.

4. For every set A, $A \cup \phi = A \cup A = A \cap A$. True or false. Explain.

5. For every set A, B, $(A \cap B) \subset A$ and $(A \cap B) \subset B$. True or false. Explain.

2 Finite Geometries

We are now about to examine two systems of axioms that exemplify, in miniature, the structure and characteristics of many modern axiomatic systems. These systems, both of which were introduced at the turn of the twentieth century, have by now attained the stature of classics in the history of mathematics. Except for phrasing (and one omission—we have left out one axiom that will be added at the end of the chapter), they are the systems of J. W. Young and G. Fano. We will see that the two systems have much in common while being quite different. By analyzing, comparing, and modifying them, it is hoped that one will gain a better understanding of exactly what an axiomatic system is.[1]

2.1 Axiom Sets 1 and 2

In first stating the two sets of axioms, we present them in what might be called their "natural" or common language phrasing. Young's axiom set is listed first:

Axiom Set 1

1. There is exactly one line through any two points.
2. Every line contains at least three points.
3. There exists at least one line.
4. Not all points are on the same line.

---

[1] By an "axiomatic system," or "system of axioms," we mean the entire structure made up of axioms, theorems, and definitions. By an "axiom set" we mean merely "the set of axioms." It may not be good English to use "axiom" as an adjective, but it is common in mathematics.

5. Through a point not on a given line, there is exactly one line which does not meet the given line.

Axiom Set 2

1. There exists at least one line.
2. Every line contains at least three points.
3. There is exactly one line through any two points.
4. Not all points are on the same line.
5. Any two lines have a point in common.

Even a cursory glance at the lists shows us that they have much in common. Indeed, except for the order in which they occur, the first four axioms are the same in both sets. And even at this stage of our presentation it should be obvious that a system of axioms is not essentially changed when the order in which the axioms are written down is rearranged. The sets differ, then, only in the fifth axiom; it shall be interesting to see how much this affects each system, how it introduces new theorems into each system; before attempting proofs, however, we would like to make some changes for the sake of clarity.

First, a word about the use of "point" and "line." In modern systems the words "point" and "line" are often not used at all, at least not in the first presentation. Instead, one might simply use "x's" and "y's"; another favorite substitute is such nonsense words as "abba" and "dabba." This is to stress the fact that the words "point" and "line" are truly undefined terms and that no other properties whatsoever can be assumed about these terms except what is given by the axioms.

An offshoot of this is that, whatever a "point" is, a "line" is going to be some kind of collection of "points" (because they are undefined terms, it could be the other way around). Thus, whatever "points" are, they can be considered as elements of some universal set; a "line" may then be regarded as some *undefined subset* of the universal set. With this approach, new words may be substituted for "point" and "line" respectively, as follows: "element of" and "l-set"; "bead" and "wire"; "man" and "committee"; and so forth. In effect, this sets up a relationship between the two undefined terms that could be introduced into the system as the following *axiom:* every line is a set of points. We are not going to adopt this procedure at the present time, but should point out that the statement is indeed an axiom and not merely a definition, as one might be tempted to think. To see that it is not a definition, one needs merely to observe that in most systems where this axiom could be used there will be other sets of points which are not lines, such as circles, triangles, and so on.

To summarize: in order to force one to refrain from using any familiar qualities of points and lines—qualities that may be actually false in a particular system or, at best, qualities which, while true, have not been formally introduced into the system—many modern systems use nonsense terms in place of "point" and "line". We shall not do so. For if one guards against using anything not explicitly given, it is easier for the beginner to form proofs if he has some interpretation of the undefined terms in mind He may even use diagrams, *but only if he guards against bringing in any hidden assumptions.*

It may surprise some readers to learn that nowhere, in the two axiom sets presented, is there an *explicit* guarantee that points exist. Statements such as that given above, that "every line is a set of points," and statements such as axioms 1, 2, and 5 in either set, *seem* to guarantee that points exist, but do not. This is because of the way in which such statements are translated into "if . . . then . . . ." form in modern logic. Let us look into this.

It is customary to equate several types of universal statements. Thus each of the following are interpreted as saying the same thing:

1. All lines have at least three points on them.
2. Any line has at least three points on it.
3. Each line has at least three points on it.
4. Every line has at least three points on it.

The last three are more precise, the first suggesting as it does that all lines (collectively) have at least three points on them. But generally they are accepted as saying the same thing, and mathematicians tend to equate them with still another form.

5. If l is any line, then it has at least three points on it.

In this form it is more apparent that the statement says nothing about the existence of l and hence nothing about the existence of three points. If, in addition to the above, it is known that there *exists* a line l, it could then be concluded:

Some line has three points on it.

or

There exists a line l with three points on it.

To sum up: universal statements (of the types 1–5, above) are not existential.

Now let us restate the two axiom sets and renumber them for future use.

Axiom Set 1

1a. If P and Q are any two points, then there exists at least one line containing both P and Q.

1b. If P and Q are any two points, then there exists at most one line containing both P and Q.

2. If l is a line, then there exist at least three points on it.

3. If l is a line, then there exists a point P not on it.

4. There exists at least one line.

5a. If l is a line and P a point not on it, then there exists at least one line m through P with no point in common with l.

5b. If l is a line and P a point not on it, then there exists at most one line m through P with no point in common with l.

Axiom Set 2

1a. If P and Q are any two points, then there exists at least one line containing both P and Q.

1b. If P and Q are any two points, then there exists at most one line containing both P and Q.

2. If l is a line, then there exist at least three points on it.

3. If l is a line, then there exists a point P not on it.

4. There exists at least one line.

5. If l and m are any two lines, then there exists at least one point P belonging to both l and m.

As is more apparent in this reworded version, only Axiom 4 is an existence statement. The others merely say "if . . . then . . . ," without guaranteeing the existence of the "if" part of the statement. Without Axiom 4, both systems would be empty of both "points" and "lines," because nothing can be assumed about these concepts, let alone something as essential as their existence.

It will pay the reader to study the restatements of these axioms. We shall, from time to time throughout the book, make a statement first in its "natural" form. Then, for the sake of clarity, and perhaps for ease of reference, we shall restate it. The restatement of Axiom 1 and Axiom 5 into two parts is an example of a device often used to prove theorems in mathematics. It depends on equating the phrase "there exists exactly one" with the conjunction of two statements: "there exists at least one" and "there exists at most one."

2.2 An Axiomatic System, 3

Now let us consider the set of *all* axioms that Axiom Set 1 and Axiom Set 2 have in common. We might have chosen any subset of *each* or *any* common subset, but there is a reason for our present choice. For future reference let us list them and call them Axiom Set 3.

Axiom Set 3

1a. If P and Q are any two points, then there exists at least one line containing both P and Q.
1b. If P and Q are any two points, then there exists at most one line containing both P and Q.
2. If l is a line, then there exist at least three points on it.
3. If l is a line, then there exists a point P not on it.
4. There exists at least one line.

Before theorems can be proved from these axioms—in fact, before the axioms can be understood—the following rules of language are needed:

Language Rule: *If a point P is an element of the line l, then we say variously:* l PASSES THROUGH $P:$ l CONTAINS $P:$ P IS ON $l;$ P LIES ON l.

Language Rule: *If a point P is an element of more than one line, then we may say:* l MEETS m in $P;$ l INTERSECTS m. (ϕ *not allowed*).

In a less simple system than the one being examined, many definitions and rules would be introduced. Such definitions might be avoided, but only at the expense of a great amount of wordiness and stilted phrasing.

We are now ready for some theorems. Proving theorems is difficult enough, the reader might be thinking; how does one go about *discovering* what theorems one is going to prove? In examining a system of axioms we must ask, first, why one chooses the axioms one does and, second, what theorems it is possible to prove from them. These questions are often ignored, not because they lack interest or importance, but because it is difficult, if not impossible, to present a workable answer. Choosing a useful set of axioms and discovering the theorems they imply is a creative act. It is as creative as anything in literature or painting, or any of the other recognized creative arts.

Our present undertaking, however, is more modest. We have observed that the existence of points in our system is not *explicitly* given; their existence is assured, however, by the following theorem:

Theorem 1. There exist at least three distinct points.

Proof: Follows immediately from Axiom 4 and Axiom 2.   ●

This theorem suggests the following analogous theorem:

Theorem 2. There exist at least three distinct lines.

Proof: By Axiom 4 there exists a line l and by Axiom 2 it has at least three points, say P, Q, and R. By Axiom 3 there exists a point, say S, not on l, and by Axiom 1a and Axiom 1b there is exactly one line through each of the pairs: PS, QS, RS. Moreover, these lines are distinct. For suppose any two of them were equal, say $SR = SQ$; then there would be two lines containing QR, namely PQR and SQR, contradicting Axiom 1b. This would be true, similarly, if $SR = SP$ or $SQ = SP$. Hence, there exist at least three distinct lines. ●

An examination of the above proof not only shows that we have proved more than we set out to prove (that there exist four distinct lines), but shows that, in the process, we did not use Theorem 1.   It therefore would have been possible to prove the second one first; the numbers of the theorems are not important. But should not Theorem 2 depend upon Theorem 1, and 3 upon 2 and 1, and so on? Not necessarily. In a very simple system, everything can be proved directly from the axioms. In fact, in any system one can in theory prove any theorem directly from the axioms (and definitions); however, the theorems are usually a convenient shortcut to proofs. And once one begins to cite theorems as reasons for steps, care must be taken about the ordering lest, in a proof, a theorem is used that in turn is proved by using the theorem that is in the process of being proved. This is circular reasoning; it is worse than circular definitions.

In the search for more theorems, the following questions are likely to occur after proving the first two theorems: How many points (lines) are there on a line (point)? Is there a finite number and, if so, can it be determined? How many points (lines) are there in the system? After exploring these questions, one discovers one can prove a related theorem:

Theorem 3. There exist at least seven points and seven lines.

Proof: By Axiom 4 there exists at least one line, which by Axiom 2 has at least three points on it. Let us designate points by A, B, C, D, . . . and lines by AB . . . (for this proof). Then, by Axiom 1a and Axiom 1b, there is a unique line containing the three points, say ABC; it is, for example, the only line containing both A and C.

Since by Axiom 3 not all points are on the same line, there exists a point D which is not on ABC.   And now by Axiom 1a, D must lie on a line with A, a line which by Axiom 2 must have at least three points on it, and which by Axiom 1b cannot contain either B or C. Hence, there exists a line ADE and, furthermore, A, B, C, D, and E are distinct. By similar arguing there exists a line BDF and A, B, C, D, E, and F are distinct.

So far we have three lines, ABC, ADE, and BDF and six points. By Axiom 1a every pair of points must have a line containing them. Point A now lies on a line with B, C, D, and E and hence must lie on a line with F; but this line must have at least one more point, and by Axiom 1b it cannot be B, C, D, or E, so there must exist another point G such that AFG.

Thus, there exist at least seven points.

Continuing in this manner, we have ABC, ADE, BDF, and AFG and at least seven points. By Axiom 1a the following possible lines must be considered: $BE \ldots$, $BG \ldots$, $EG \ldots$, $CD \ldots$, $CG \ldots$, $DG \ldots$, $CE \ldots$, $CF \ldots$, $EF \ldots$. Consider line $BE \ldots$. By Axiom 1b it can contain only G from the given choice of points, and by Axiom 2 it must; hence we have a new line, BEG. (Axiom 1b now rules out $BG \ldots$ and $EG \ldots$).

Now consider $CD \ldots$. By Axiom 1b and Axiom 2 it must contain G; so we have a new line CDG. (And Axiom 1b rules out $CG \ldots$ and $DG \ldots$). By Axiom 1b and Axiom 2, $CE \ldots$ must contain F, giving us CEF. (And Axiom 1b rules out $CF \ldots$, and $EF \ldots$). Hence we have generated distinct lines: ABC, ADE, BDF, AFG, BEG, CDG, and CEF.

Thus, there exist at least seven lines. ● (Can we prove this theorem for $n > 7$? See Exercises 2.2)

Continuing in this manner, and keeping in mind that we are dealing with undefined terms, we might ask other questions that we ordinarily might not think of. We might, for example, ask the number of points which two lines may have in common; must they have any? If so, how many?

If we set out to answer the question, "must two lines have any points in common?", we will arrive at an interesting answer. We need merely observe that the fifth axioms of Axiom Sets 1 and 2 answer this question both negatively and affirmatively. It would seem likely, therefore, that this question cannot be answered at all from Axiom Set 3, unless there is reason to believe that one of the axioms numbered "5" can be proved as a theorem and is therefore not an axiom. If one can show that none of the axioms in either Set 1 or Set 2 can be proved as a theorem; specifically, if it can be shown that Axioms 5a and 5b of Set I are not implied by Axiom Set 3; and if it can further be shown that Axiom 5 of Set 2 cannot be derived from Axiom Set 3, then one is left with an inescapable conclusion: a question has been found phraseable in the terms of our system that is unanswerable in our system. It cannot be proved that any two lines have a point in common; contrary to this, it cannot be proved that there exist parallel lines. We shall return to this interesting problem in the next chapter.

If we now turn to the question, "what is the *most* number of points two lines may have in common?", the answer is not so difficult. It will be given after the next section.

EXERCISES 2.2

Using Axiom Set 3, try to prove the following:

1. There exist at least 8 points.
2. There exist at least 4 points on a line.
3. There exists at least one pair of nonintersecting lines.

2.3 Direct and Indirect Proofs

We have just seen some examples of proofs. To better understand them, let us take a look at their skeletal forms. First, we shall look at direct proofs, which for our present purposes can be regarded as falling simply into two patterns:

$$\text{(a)} \quad \frac{\begin{array}{l} \text{If } P \text{ then } Q \\ P \end{array}}{Q} \qquad \text{(b)} \quad \frac{\begin{array}{l} \text{If } P \text{ then } Q \\ \text{not-}Q \end{array}}{\text{not-}P}$$

These are called *valid-argument* patterns. They say that if the two statements above the line are granted, the statement below the line is an inescapable conclusion or, alternatively, that it *follows from* the first two. Stated in such terms, there are overtones of mental processes at work. So instead, we shall say, "If P then Q, and P" implies "Q," and "If P then Q and not-Q" implies "not-P." Keeping in mind that "implies" is to be regarded as an undefined relation, it is useful to point out that these two patterns illustrate one of the properties the relation is to have: that true statements cannot imply false statements.

A fallacy occurs when the valid patterns (a) and (b) are confused with the following invalid ones:

$$\text{(c)} \quad \frac{\begin{array}{l} \text{If } P \text{ then } Q \\ Q \end{array}}{P} \qquad \text{(d)} \quad \frac{\begin{array}{l} \text{If } P \text{ then } Q \\ \text{not-}P \end{array}}{\text{not-}Q}$$

The easiest way to commit this error is to confuse a conditional statement with its converse.

The patterns (a) and (b) are by no means the only valid direct argument patterns but they are the only ones we shall introduce for now. It is surprising how far we can go with just these and equivalent variations of them when we introduce a property of implication that permits us to build long chains of such patterns. This property of implication is called *transitivity:* if A implies B, and B implies C, then A implies C.

Directing our attention now to indirect proofs, we shall see that this type of proof is based on a property of implication just mentioned: it is impossible for a true statement to imply a false statement. Let us see how this works.

Suppose one wishes to prove the statement:

(a) If P then Q.

One starts by assuming its contradictory; specifically, assume:

(b) P and not-Q.

If statement (b) implies a statement known to be false, then statement (b) must *be* a false statement—for it is impossible for a true statement to imply a false statement. But, if the statement (b) is false, then statement (a), its contradictory, must be true; hence, in this manner, "If P then Q" has been shown to be true.

The phrase "if statement (b) implies a statement known to be false" used in the preceding explanation requires some comment. First, rarely in mathematics does a single statement imply another. Usually, when it is said that a statement implies another, this means that a statement, together with others (assumed or previously proved), imply the second statement. Secondly, a contradiction may be reached in several ways. As soon as the truth of "P and not-Q" is assumed, it follows from the definition of conjunction that both "P" and "not-Q" hold; therefore, a contradiction is obtained in any one of the following ways: (1) "P and not-Q" *implies* "not-P"; (2) "P and not-Q" *implies* "Q"; or, (3) "P and not-Q" *implies* "R and not-R." In any one of these cases the assumption "P and not-Q" must be false.

The most common error one makes in using an *indirect proof* (which we are using synonymously with *proof by contradiction*) is to use *any* denial of the universal statement rather than its contradictory. Suppose, for example, we are trying to prove that two line segments $\overline{AB}$ and $\overline{CD}$ are equal, and suppose we assume that $\overline{AB}$ is greater than $\overline{CD}$, giving us a contradiction; this does not then entitle us to claim that the two segments are equal, for it is still possible that $\overline{AB}$ might be less than $\overline{CD}$. Whenever the contradiction of a statement is not used in a proof, one must be careful to take into account all the possible cases.

Universal statements in various forms have already been discussed.

For illustrative purposes, consider "Every line has at least three points on it." The contradiction of this is not "No line has three points on it"— nor can it be stated as "There exists a line with only one point on it." Both of these are contraries rather than contradictories. The contradictory would be "There exists a line which does not have at least three points on it" or "There exists a line with at most two points on it."

One final remark is in order. Our comments so far have been concerned with attempts to prove a universal statement true. In order to prove one false, one need only find a single *counterexample*, a single instance of its falsity.

Before going on to prove more theorems, let us return to Theorem 2 for a brief analysis. A brief look at the proof seems to show us that it is both direct and indirect. The first half is direct and the second half appears to be indirect. But this is only apparently so. We shall consider this a direct proof. The only proof which we will call *indirect* is one which begins immediately by contradicting (or denying and considering all cases) the statement we are attempting to prove. Let us analyze the proof step by step.

STEP 1: Axiom 2 together with Axiom 4 is an instance of argument form (a).

STEP 2: Axiom 3 together with Axiom 4 is another instance of pattern (a).

STEP 3: Axioms 1a and 1b together with the results of Steps 1 and 2 are another instance of pattern (a).

It now remains to prove that the three lines are distinct. Instead of incorporating this into the proof, suppose we take it aside and prove a helping theorem, called a *lemma*.

Lemma 1: *Suppose there exist three points P, Q, R on a line, a point S not on the line, and three lines PS, QS, and RS joining these points; then these lines are distinct.*
Proof: Same as given.

We can now give the *direct* proof of Theorem 2: Steps 1, 2, 3 and Lemma 1.

2.4   Further Proofs in Axiomatic System 3

We cannot easily continue our heuristic approach to geometry without creating a mass of confusion. This type of unordered thinking—asking about possible theorems, hunting and finding them by trial and error, and trying to discover proofs for them—goes into creating a system, but once the discoveries have been made we must present the theorems in an orderly manner. Let us attempt to do that now.

Theorem 4. Two lines have at most one point in common.

Restatement: *If l and m are any two lines, then there exists at most one point P in their intersection.*
Proof: Suppose the statement is false. Then there exist two lines *l* and *m* which have at least two points, say *P* and *Q*, in common. But this immediately contradicts Axiom 1b, for *l* contains *P* and *Q*, and *m* contains *P* and *Q*, and Axiom 1b says that at most one line contains two given points. The assumption that our statement is false leads to a contradiction, so we conclude: two lines have at most one point in common.   •

(NOTE: We have been using an unstated convention. Whenever we speak of points *P*, *Q*, or lines *m*, *n*, it is possible they may be the same; but whenever we speak of the *two* points *P*, *Q*, or two lines *m*, *n*, we mean them to be distinct.)

To further illustrate the differences in techniques of direct and indirect proofs, we shall prove the next theorem both directly and indirectly.

Theorem 5. Not all lines pass through the same point.

Restatement: *If P is a point, then there exists at least one line not containing P.*
Direct Proof: Let *P* be a point. This may be said because by Theorem 1 points are known to exist. By the same theorem there exists a second point *Q*. Now by Axiom 1a there exists a line *l* containing *P* and *Q*. By Axiom 3 there exists a point *R* not on *l* and by Axiom 1a there exists a line *m* containing *Q* and *R*. Because *R* is not on *l*, *l* and *m* are distinct. Now if *P* belongs to *m*, then there exist distinct lines with two points in common, contradicting Theorem 4. Hence, *m* is a line not containing *P*.   •

As stated previously, we call this a direct proof despite the contradiction used to prove that *P* does not belong to *m*. We are calling any proof direct if it does not rest on assuming that the statement being proved is false.

Indirect Proof: Suppose that every line passes through the same point *P*. By Theorem 2 there exist at least two lines. If they are to pass through *P* and be distinct, they must contain points not in common, so let us say that *l* contains *P* and *Q* and *m* contains *P* and *R*. By Axiom 1a there exists a line, say *k*, containing *Q* and *R*; by assumption, it must contain *P*. But this contradicts Theorem 4. Hence, our assumption that every line passes through P must be false. Hence, there exists at least one line not through P. ●

Theorem 6. There exist at least three lines through any point.

Restatement: *If P is any point, there exist at least three lines through P.*
Proof: Suppose that there exists a point P with at most two lines through it, call them l (containing P and Q) and m (containing P and R). By Theorem 5 there exists a line not through P. If this line does not contain Q and R, then it contains three other points by Axiom 2, and by Axiom 1a there exist at least three more lines containing these points and P. If, on the other hand, the line not containing P does contain Q or R, then by Axiom 2 it contains at least one other point S and, once again by Axiom 1a, there exists another line containing P and S. In either case our assumption is contradicted. Hence there exist at least three lines through any point. ●

Note that while our proof classifies as indirect in this case, we are actually obtaining our contradiction by showing the existence of a third line. This suggests that a direct proof is certainly possible and may even be simpler, but this is left to be solved as an exercise. Instead, we will show how a slight change in the proof of Theorem 6 gives us another indirect proof.

Theorem 6 (*Alternative*)
Proof: Suppose that there exists a point P with at most two lines through it, call them l (containing P and Q) and m (containing P and R). By Theorem 5 there exists a line not through P. Whether this line contains Q and R or not, there exists a new point on it, call it S. But by our assumption there cannot be another line containing P, and this now contradicts Axiom 1a. Hence our assumption is false and there exist at least three lines through any point. ●

EXERCISES 2.4

1. Can you prove from Axiom Set 3 that there exist at most seven points?
2. Can you prove from Axiom Set 3 that there exist at most three points on a line?
3. Can you prove from Axiom Set 3 that any two lines must intersect?
4. Give a direct proof of Theorem 6.

5. Analyze each of the indirect proofs given in this section. Which of the three types listed in Section 2.3 is each?

6. What is wrong with the following direct "proof" of Theorem 6?

Proof: By Axiom 4 there exists a line; by Axiom 2 it has three points on it, call them P, Q, R; by Axiom 3 there exists a point S not on the line and by Axiom 1a there exist three lines PS, QS, and RS through S.

7. Can the "proof" in exercise 6 be revised to correct it?

2.5   Axiomatic System 1

In the exercises in the preceding sections it was suggested that one try to prove that there exists at least one pair of nonintersecting lines and that there exist at least eight points. We trust that attempts to prove these statements were not successful.

Let us now convert Axiom Set 3 back into Axiom Set 1 by adding Axioms 5a and 5b in order to see what new theorems we can prove. Using Axiom Set 1 we may derive the following:

Theorem 7. There exist at least nine points and at least twelve lines.

Proof: Left as an exercise.

Definition. Two lines l and m are called *parallel* if l and m have no point in common.

Theorem 8. There exist at least two lines parallel to a given line.

Proof: By Axiom 4 there exists at least one line l; by Axiom 3 there exists a point P not on l; by Axiom 5a there exists at least one line m parallel to l through P. By Axiom 2 there exists at least one point Q on l and by Axiom 1a there exists a line PQ, which by Axiom 2 has a third point S on it. By Axiom 5a there exists a line k through S, parallel to l. These lines must be distinct. (Why?) ●

Theorem 9. If a line intersects one of two parallels, it must intersect the other.

Restatement: *If k and l are two parallels, and m intersects k at a point P, then m intersects l at some point.*

Proof: Suppose not. Then through P there would be two lines m and k not intersecting l. But this contradicts Axiom 5b. Hence the assumption must be false and thus, if a line intersects one of two parallels, it intersects the other. ●

Theorem 10. Two lines parallel to the same line are parallel to each other.

Restatement: *If k and l are parallel and l and m are parallel, then k and m are parallel.*
Proof: Suppose not. If k is not parallel to m, then it intersects m and by Theorem 9 must then also intersect l, contradicting our assumption that it is parallel to l. Hence our assumption must be false. So two lines parallel to the same line must be parallel to each other. ●

Before attempting a proof of the next theorem, let us take time to look back at some of the preceding proofs. It is likely that those who attempted to follow proofs of Theorems 7 and 8 very closely had to resort to some kind of visual aid. We have purposely omitted diagrams up to now in order to force the reader to fend for himself. In a proof as difficult as the next one, however, it is *almost* necessary to use a diagram to construct the proof and to follow it. We say "almost" because it is never necessary; a diagram is merely an aid to one's intuition and not a part of a proof. As an aid, it is perfectly all right to use a diagram at any time, but observe the warning mentioned earlier and do not, in using a diagram, bring in any hidden assumptions. In a proof such as the following it is easy to transgress on this rule without even being aware of it.

Because the proof is a long one, we shall break it up into two lemmas. We have already indicated that a *lemma* is a theorem proved primarily to help prove some other theorem. Generally, it is called a *lemma* when its use is more or less restricted to the theorem in question; if it had other uses, one would usually call it a theorem and give it an appropriate number. (We assume knowledge of the properties of the natural numbers.) The reader may refer to Figure 2.1.

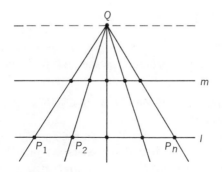

FIGURE 2.1

Lemma 1: *If one line l contains exactly n points, then any line parallel to l contains exactly n points.*

Proof: Suppose l is a line containing exactly n points $P_1, P_2, \cdots, P_n$. Since by Theorem 8 there exist other lines parallel to l, we may let m be any line parallel to l. Once again by Theorem 8 there exists still another line, parallel to both m and l, and by Axiom 2 it has a point Q on it, which by the definition of parallel cannot be on either m or l. Now by Axiom 1a there exist lines $QP_1, QP_2, \cdots, QP_n$, which by Axiom 1b are distinct. By Theorem 9 these lines intersect m and by Theorem 4 it must be in n distinct points. Hence there exist at least n distinct points on m.

Suppose there exists another point on m, say P_{n+1}. Then there must be a line connecting Q with P_{n+1}, and by Theorem 9 and Theorem 4 it must intersect l in some point other than $P_1, P_2, \cdots, P_n$, contradicting the assumption that l has exactly n points. Hence there exist at most n distinct points on m.

The lemma now follows.   ●

The reader should fill in the steps, mostly justifications, that have been left out of the above proof, and should convince himself that the locations of Q, m, and l in the diagram are immaterial. We could choose Q as shown in Figure 2.2, or any other of the possible arrangements of Q, m and l. It

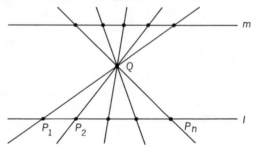

FIGURE 2.2

is the power of Theorem 9 that assures us that we shall obtain our n points on m regardless of where Q is located. To follow the next proof refer to Figure 2.3.

Lemma 2: *If any line l contains exactly n points, then there exist exactly $n - 1$ lines parallel to l.*

Proof: Let l be a line with exactly n points $P_1, P_2, \cdots, P_n$ on it and let Q be a point not on l. Then there exists a line QP_1 and another line QP_i (where i is any of the n points other than P_1). By Axioms 5a and 5b there exist exactly $n - 1$ lines through $P_2, \cdots, P_n$ that are parallel to

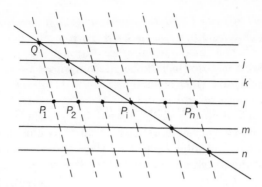

FIGURE 2.3

QP_1 (one of which will pass through P_i). By Theorem 9 and Theorem 4, QP_i, which intersects QP_1 and the line parallel to it through P_i, must intersect each of the other lines in exactly one point. Hence, there exist exactly n points on line QP_i.

By Axioms 5a and 5b and Theorem 4 there exist *exactly* $n - 1$ parallels to l (Why?). ●

Theorem 11. If one line contains exactly n points, then every line contains exactly n points.

Proof: Given a line l with exactly n points on it, any line either intersects l or does not. If it does not, then by Lemma 1 it has exactly n points on it. If it does intersect l, then by Theorem 9 it intersects the $n - 1$ lines parallel to l, lines that exist by Lemma 2; by Theorem 4 it intersects in exactly n points. Hence, if one line contains exactly n points, every line does. ●

EXERCISES 2.5

1. Prove Theorem 7.
2. Can you prove that there exist *at most* nine points?
3. Complete the proofs of the two lemmas.
4. Prove: If there exists one line with exactly n points, then every point has exactly $n + 1$ lines through it.

Using Axiom Set 2, prove the following:

5. If there exists one line with exactly n points on it, then every line contains exactly n points.
6. If there exists one line with exactly n points on it, then every point has exactly n lines through it.

2.6   The Systems of Young and Fano

If to Axiom Set 1 we add the following axiom we get the original system credited to Young.

Axiom 6. If l is a line, there exist at most three points on it.

We shall refer to this system as the System of Young. The addition of this last axiom has a profound effect on the system; it makes it a finite geometry, as is illustrated by the next three theorems.

Theorem 12Y. There exist exactly nine points in the system.

Proof: Left as an exercise.

Theorem 13Y. There exist exactly twelve lines in the system.

Proof: Left as an exercise.

Theorem 14Y. There exist exactly four lines through any point.

Proof: Left as an exercise.

If now the same Axiom 6 is added to Axiom Set 2, the system originally credited to Fano is obtained. We shall refer to this system as the System of Fano. It, too, is a finite system but, as one might expect, of a different nature than the System of Young.

Using now the System of Fano, we can prove:

Theorem 12F. There exist exactly seven points.

Proof: Left as an exercise.

Theorem 13F. There exist exactly seven lines.

Proof: Left as an exercise.

Theorem 14F. There exist exactly three lines through any point.

Proof: Left as an exercise.

EXERCISES 2.6

1–6. Prove Theorems 12Y, 13Y, 14Y, 12F, 13F, and 14F.

7. Suppose one adds Axiom 6 to Axiom Set 3; at most, how many points and lines do you suppose one can prove to exist?

3 Properties of Axiomatic Systems

Now that the reader has been introduced to several particular systems of axioms he should be able to understand an abstract discussion of axiomatic systems in general. There are three important concepts usually associated with any axiomatic system: consistency, independence, and completeness. A discussion of these topics, using the systems introduced in Chapter 2 as examples, will provide answers to the questions raised in that chapter.

3.1 Consistency

If the purpose of language is to communicate, it is self-defeating if something is said and then "un-said." This is what is done when one says "*P* and not-*P*." In order to express this more precisely, let us first review what has previously been said about sentences.

First, recall that not all sentences are true or false. Even when such nonsense as "All triangles are courageous" and such exclamations as "Shut the door!" are excluded, a very important type of sentence remains, one to which we cannot apply the words true or false. For example, when one says, "He has red hair" or "X is an even number," such sentences, strictly speaking, cannot be said to be either true or false. In today's parlance, they are called *open sentences*. That is, they are sentences that become *statements*, become true or false, when the "variables" in the sentence are assigned some definite referent. Thus, "George Brown has red hair" and "Seven is an even number" are no longer open sentences; they are *statements*, or *propositions* (we use the two words synonymously); they are sentences that are either true or false. All sentences in mathematics are (or should be) either open sentences or statements.

With this agreement, the classical laws of logic hold:

The Law of Contradiction: *No statement can be both true and false.*

The Law of Excluded Middle: *Every statement is either true or false.*

Now let us return to our first point. If P is a statement, then when we say "P and not-P" we are not merely making a false statement; we are saying something and retracting it. We are in effect saying nothing or, to put it another way, we are breaking our rules of language and thus speaking nonsense. Therefore, in a system of axioms one may permit any number of statements to be false if one chooses but one must never allow any two statements to be of the type "P" and "not-P." This can be said more succinctly if we introduce the following definition:

Definition. An axiom system is *consistent* iff there do not exist in the system any two axioms, any axiom and theorem, or any two theorems of the form "P" and "not-P."

Using this definition we can now summarize: **it is absolutely essential for an axiomatic system to be consistent.**

Very well, but how does one determine this? What is being said, in effect, is that for an axiomatic system to be consistent it must be impossible to ever prove a theorem contradicting another theorem or axiom. Unless one has reason to believe that one has already proved every single theorem that it is possible to prove from a given set of axioms, there is no way of knowing whether or not a contradiction will be discovered just ahead. And even if one knew one had derived every theorem, might there not be so many of them, or might they not be so complex or so subtle, that a contradiction might rest inextricably hidden among them? How can one be sure? This is a question to which there is no definitive answer.

There is, however, a pragmatic test for consistency that mathematicians have been using for years. To explain precisely how the test works, it will be helpful to introduce a few definitions and then to use the axiomatic systems of the preceding chapter to illustrate the test.

The systems introduced as Axiom Set 1 and Axiom Set 2 are "abstract systems" as long as the terms "point" and "line" are taken as undefined. As long as these terms remain undefined the axioms are open sentences. It is not until some meaning is given to the undefined terms that one may legitimately ask whether the axioms are true or false.

Definition. By an *interpretation* of an axiomatic system we mean: the assignment of meanings to the undefined technical terms in such a way that the axioms become either true or false.

Definition. An interpretation that makes an axiom *true* is said to *satisfy* that axiom. If there exists an interpretation in which every axiom in a set becomes true, then the set is said to be *satisfiable*.

Definition. If a set is satisfiable, then such an interpretation is called a *model*.

Test for Consistency: *If there exists a model for a set of axioms, the set is consistent.*

The existence of a model as a test for consistency may be justified as follows. If one can find such a model, then all axioms in the system become true statements. Hence all statements implied by the axioms—that is, all theorems—must become true statements because it is impossible for a true statement to imply a false statement. If each axiom is true, then the conjunction of all axioms is a true statement and anything implied by this conjunction of statements must itself be true by the laws of logic.

Some examples should clarify how the model test for consistency works.

3.2 Models for Consistency

Suppose that a college offers the following challenge to its best students. The top three members of each class, sophomore, junior, and senior, will be given an all-expense-paid trip to nine countries whose political attitudes toward the United States are either neutral or negative. On their return they must debate and discuss what they have learned.

To make the project challenging, the three discussion teams will be made up solely of classmates. To make it fair, but not too time-consuming, the teams are divided into sets of three, with one member of each class on a team and each of the three teams to spend one week in a country. They will regroup in such a way that no two men are ever on the same team; the new teams will then spend one week in another country. For clarity, the students make up the following chart:

Sophomores: Alan, Bob, Charley
Juniors: Dick, Ernie, Fred
Seniors: George, Herm, Irving
Algeria: Alan, Dick, George
Bulgaria: Bob, Ernie, Irving
Cambodia: Charley, Fred, Herm
Dominican Republic: Alan, Ernie, Herm
Egypt: Bob, Fred, George
Finland: Charley, Dick, Irving

Ghana: Alan, Fred, Irving
Hungary: Bob, Dick, Herm
India: Charley, Ernie, George

The interpretation should be obvious: "point" = student; "line" = team; "belonging to" = is a member of.

This interpretation will be seen to be a model for Axiom Set 1. The reader should check carefully to be convinced that each of the axioms of the system is satisfied by this interpretation. The same holds for the following three models, which are listed for future reference:

Model II (9 points, 12 lines)

1	4	1	1	1	2	2	2	3	3	3	7
2	5	4	5	6	4	5	6	4	5	6	8
3	6	9	7	8	7	8	9	8	9	7	9

In this model "points" are numbers and "lines" are columns of numbers.

Model III (16 points, 20 lines)

1	5	1	1	1	1	2	2	2	2	3	3	3	3	4	4	4	4	9	10
2	6	5	6	7	8	5	6	7	8	5	6	7	8	5	6	7	8	11	12
3	7	9	10	11	12	10	11	12	9	11	15	9	13	14	9	13	10	14	13
4	8	13	14	15	16	16	13	14	15	12	16	10	14	15	12	16	11	16	15

Model IV (Infinite points, lines)
Ordinary Euclidean geometry

Even if it is now apparent that these are indeed models and that therefore all theorems provable in the system must be true, doubts remain as to the reliability of using such criteria. This is especially so when the model has an infinite number of elements, as in Model IV. How does one know that it really satisfies Axioms 1a and 1b and the others? It would take an infinite number of checks to find out. How does one know that the very model being used to guarantee consistency is not itself inconsistent? In such cases only a relative type of test for consistency has been found. All that can be said is that if Euclidean geometry is consistent, then so is that system for which it is a model—and in several thousand years no one has discovered an inconsistency in Euclidean geometry; therefore, it is probably consistent. Unfortunately, such relative tests will always be required when one is dealing with any system with an infinite number of elements. In the case of finite models such as the first three given above, it is not too difficult to check for hidden problems because one can check every case. Such models have sometimes been said to be "absolute" tests for consistency.

Let us look at a few more models, this time for Axiom Set 2.

Suppose that a mathematics department has seven faculty members and suppose they decide to form seven committees to study and determine the best way to teach specific topics in axiomatic geometry. It is agreed, for the sake of fairness, that each member will be the chairman of one committee and serve on exactly two others and that each committee will have exactly three members. They draw up the following chart:

Committee to Study	Chairman	Members	
Axioms	Appolonius	Bolyai	Ceva
Betweenness	Bolyai	Desargues	Fano
Congruence	Ceva	Desargues	Euclid
Dissection theory	Desargues	Appolonius	Gauss
Equivalence relations	Euclid	Appolonius	Fano
Finite systems	Fano	Gauss	Ceva
Geometries, infinite	Gauss	Euclid	Bolyai

With the interpretation that "points" are the mathematicians and "lines" the committees as listed in each row, an examination of this chart will show that every axiom of Set 2 is satisfied. Switching the members in the second and third columns may be of help in checking but it is not necessary. Call this Model V.

As another interpretation consider the following. A manufacturer is interested in making a trinket made up of seven beads, each of a different color. He wishes to join them to seven wires in such a way that there are three beads on each wire and three wires through each bead. He makes up the following list: amber, yellow, red, blue, green, orange, and violet. The trinket looks like Figure 3.1.

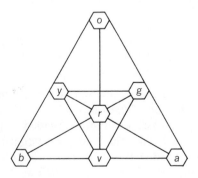

FIGURE 3.1

With the interpretation that "point" = bead, "line" = wire, and the wires and beads arranged as in Figure 3.1, they can be listed:

$W_1 = \{b, y, o\}$ $W_2 = \{a, g, o\}$ $W_3 = \{a, y, r\}$ $W_4 = \{b, g, r\}$

$W_5 = \{a, b, v\}$ $W_6 = \{y, g, v\}$ $W_7 = \{o, r, v\}$

One finds on examination that this is another model for System 2. Call it Model VI.

For another interpretation, take the following array of numbers:

$$
\begin{array}{ccccccc}
1 & 2 & 3 & 4 & 5 & 6 & 7 \\
2 & 3 & 4 & 5 & 6 & 7 & 1 \\
4 & 5 & 6 & 7 & 1 & 2 & 3
\end{array}
$$

in which a "point" = a number and "line" = a column. Since this interpretation also makes all the axioms true, it may be considered Model VII.

For a final interpretation:

$$
\begin{array}{ccccccccccccc}
A & B & C & D & E & F & G & H & I & J & K & L & M \\
B & C & D & E & F & G & H & I & J & K & L & M & A \\
D & E & F & G & H & I & J & K & L & M & A & B & C \\
J & K & L & M & A & B & C & D & E & F & G & H & I
\end{array}
$$

where once again "point" = letter of the alphabet and "line" = column. This interpretation also makes each of the axioms a true statement; call it Model VIII.

We have now listed eight models, four models for each of our two axiom sets. Each model is sufficient to show the consistency of its respective system. In addition, it should be apparent that all eight interpretations are models for Axiom Set 3. It is not necessary to gather so much evidence; all one needs to show consistency is a single model. However, in later discussions, we shall find other uses for some of the models listed in this section.

3.3   Independence

After a set of axioms has been chosen and it has been determined that they are consistent, the next question that arises is whether each statement is truly primitive—that it cannot be derived from the other members of the set of axioms. Stated another way, how can it be known that one of the axioms is not a theorem? When phrased in this way it might lead one to counter with another question, namely, "What if it is?" If it is, nothing is seriously wrong; at worst it might be difficult to prove and is simply left as an axiom. On the other hand, a proof might be supplied. In either case the system suffers no irreparable damage.

Does this mean that independence, as defined in the next definition, is an unnecessary property in an axiom system? Evidently. But there are many mathematicians who, for aesthetic and logical reasons, try to reduce an axiom set to a set of independent axioms. In fact, such an attempt plays a significant role in the history of mathematics, as will be apparent later.

Let us consider a new problem. Suppose one wishes to choose an independent set of axioms. How does one go about such a task? We might start with the following definition:

Definition. A statement is said to be *independent* in a set of statements if it is impossible to derive it from the other members of the set.

This is not a very practical definition, for how can one tell whether or not a statement is provable? If it has not been proven, might it still not be provable? As in the case of consistency, there is a test for independence.

Test: *If an axiom set is consistent and if, when the statement being tested is replaced by its denial there exists a model for the new set, then the statement being tested is independent.*

That is, if $A_1, \cdots, A_i, \cdots, A_n$ is consistent and if $A_1, \cdots,$ not-A_i, $\cdots, A_n$ is consistent, then A_i is independent. For if the original system is consistent and A_i is a theorem, then it is implied by the other axioms, and the contradiction of A_i together with the other axioms could not possibly be consistent; that is, there would exist no model for such a set of statements.

Let us illustrate this in Axiom Set 1. We shall find models showing the independence of each of the axioms in the set.

The following interpretation shows the independence of

Axiom 1a:

$$l = \{P_1, P_2, P_3\}$$
$$m = \{P_4, P_5, P_6\}$$

The "interpretation" is precisely what is given; namely, the two sets as "lines" and the six elements as "points." For the interpretation to test the independence of Axiom 1a it must satisfy the *negation* of Axiom 1a *and* must satisfy each of the other axioms. It certainly satisfies the negation of the first axiom because the points P_2 and P_4, for example, do not have a line containing them. A careful check will show that it satisfies the other axioms.

It should be pointed out that in negating an axiom one does not need to limit the negation to the true contradictory of the given statement; a contrary may be used as well. The difference between them, one will recall from an earlier discussion, is that of two contradictories one is true and the other is false; whereas of two contrary statements both cannot be true but it is possible for both to be false. Because a contrary will suffice to negate an axiom, one can deny Axiom 1b by finding an interpretation with two lines, three lines, four lines, and so forth, containing two given points.

Now let us find a model showing the independence of Axiom 1b. Taking the easy axioms first, we know the following: the model must have a line, the line must have at least three points, and there must exist a point not on the line. Now, to deny Axiom 1b, there must exist at least two lines containing the same two points; and, in order for the lines to be distinct, they must contain a third distinct point. So one might start with:

$$4 \quad 1$$
$$5 \quad 4$$
$$6 \quad 5$$

As before, the numbers are "points" and the columns "lines." In this interpretation, Axiom 1b is negated; Axioms 2, 3, and 4 are satisfied. But what of each of the others, which must also be satisfied? To satisfy 5a and 5b there must exist a unique parallel through any point not on a given line, and to satisfy 1a there must exist lines containing points 1 and 6 and any other points that happen to be generated in the process of satisfying the rest of the axioms. So one arrives at the independence model for

Axiom 1b:

$$
\begin{array}{cccccccccc}
1 & 4 & 1 & 2 & 2 & 1 & 2 & 1 & 3 & 1 \\
2 & 5 & 4 & 3 & 4 & 3 & 4 & 3 & 4 & 2 \\
3 & 6 & 5 & 6 & 5 & 6 & 6 & 5 & 5 & 6 \\
\end{array}
$$

(NOTE: We can add {1, 3, 4}; {2, 5, 6}; {1, 5, 6}; {2, 3, 4}; {2, 3, 5}; {1, 4, 6}; {3, 5, 6}; {1, 2, 4} and still satisfy the system.)

To complete the test for the independence of the axioms in Axiom Set 1 we cite the following models. In each instance the interpretation should be checked to verify that it is indeed a model for the independence of the axiom in question.

Axiom 2:
$$
\begin{array}{cccccc}
1 & 3 & 1 & 2 & 2 & 1 \\
2 & 4 & 4 & 4 & 3 & 3 \\
\end{array}
$$

Axiom 3: $l = \{1, 2, 3\}$

Axiom 4: a single point; no line

Axiom 5a: Any one of the models for the consistency of the Axiom Set 2. Thus we may take Models V, VI, VII, or VIII of the preceding section.

In checking to see that the interpretation is indeed a model showing the independence of Axiom 4, the question arises as to how this interpretation satisfies the other axioms. The answer lies in the fact that all of the other axioms are of the form "If . . . then . . ."; in order for them to be false, there must *exist* a line such that . . . or there must *exist* two points such that . . . . If lines do not exist, if two points do not exist, the statements cannot be false; hence they are true. This is sometimes called *vacuous* satisfaction.

Axiom 5b: Finally, for Axiom 5b we present the following rather complicated model:

1	5	5	1	1	1	1	1	2	2	2	2	2	3	3
2	6	19	5	16	7	8	12	5	6	7	8	11	5	6
3	7	15	9	6	19	10	15	16	10	12	9	13	12	19
4	8	10	13	11	14	18	17	18	14		15	19	14	9
									17					

3	3	3	4	4	4	4	4	6	7	8	9	13	17
7	8	10	5	6	7	8	9	12	9	11	10	14	18
11	17	16	11	15	10	12	18	18	16	14	11	15	19
15	13		17		13	16	14	13	17		12	16	
18					19								

It can be seen that this model has 19 points and 29 lines and that not every line has the same number of points.

It is instructive to attempt to find an independence model for Axiom 5b that has the same number of points on a line. While the proof of Theorem 11 uses Axiom 5b, is it necessary to use it? If it is, it would seem that without Axiom 5b we cannot prove that every line must have the same number of points. On the other hand, the exercises following the proof of Theorem 11 indicate that the same theorem holds in Axiom System 2, which has no Axiom 5b. Furthermore, if the proof of the independence of Axiom 5b were incompatible with all lines having the same number of points, what then of the consistency of the System of Young where we stipulate that all lines have three points? An answer to this problem might be found in the solution to Exercise 3.3.III.

In conclusion, it should be pointed out once again that independence, unlike consistency, is not essential to a system. While it is true that for aesthetic or logical reasons one might attempt to adopt independent statements as axioms, it is often not done. If a theorem is difficult to prove and is assumed as an axiom the system will not itself be ruined.

EXERCISES 3.3

I. From the following list select models showing the independence of each axiom in Axiom Set 2.

Interpretations:

1.
1	4	1	1	1	2	2	2	3	3	3	7
2	5	4	5	6	4	5	6	4	5	6	8.
3	6	9	7	8	7	8	9	8	9	7	9

2. A single point; no line.

3. $l = \{P_1, P_2, P_3\}$; $m = \{P_1, P_4, P_5\}$.

4.
1	3	1	2	2	1
2	4	4	4	3	3

5. Three points; no line.

6. $l = \{P_1, P_2\}$; $m = \{P_2, P_3\}$; $k = \{P_3, P_1\}$.

7.
1	4	1	2	2	1	2	1	3	1
2	5	4	3	4	3	4	3	4	2.
3	6	5	6	5	6	6	5	5	6

8. $k = \{P_1\}$; $l = \{P_1, P_2\}$; $m = \{P_1, P_3\}$; $n = \{P_2, P_3\}$.

9. $k = \{P_2, P_3, P_4\}$; $l = \{P_1, P_2, P_3\}$; $m = \{P_1, P_2, P_4\}$.

10. $l = \{P_1, P_3, P_2\}$.

11.
1	2	3	4	5	6	7
2	3	4	5	6	7	1.
4	5	6	7	1	2	3

12. $l = \{P_1, P_2, P_3\}$; $m = \{P_4, P_5, P_6\}$.

II. Consider the following axiom system:

1. If l and m are any two distinct lines, they have at least one point in common.

2. If P_1 and P_2 are any two distinct points, they have *at least one* line through them.

3. If P_1 and P_2 are any two distinct points, they have *at most one* line through them.

4. Not all points are on the same line.

5. There exist exactly three distinct points.

(a) By trying to find independence models for each axiom, one should be able to determine that one of the axioms is not independent.

(b) Prove it as a theorem.

III. The following two models are possible models for the independence of Axiom 5b of Axiom Set 1. Test each to see if it is.

1.

1	1	2	3	1	2	3	4	1	2	3	5	6	7	1	2	3	5
2	4	4	4	6	7	5	8	10	8	8	8	8	8	9	9	9	9
3	5	6	7	7	5	6	9	8	11	12	13	14	15	11	12	13	14

6	7	2	3	4	5	6	3	4	6	7	1	5	7	1	4	2
9	9	10	10	10	10	10	11	11	11	11	12	12	12	13	13	14
15	10	13	14	15	11	12	15	12	13	14	14	15	13	15	14	15

2.

1	1	1	1	1	1	1	1	1		2	2	2	2	2	2	2	2
2	4	5	6	12	13	15	17	10		4	5	6	10	11	14	15	16
3	7	8	9	14	16	18	19	11		8	9	7	12	13	18	19	17

3	3	3	3	3	3	3	3		4	4	4	4	4	4
4	5	6	10	11	12	16	17		5	10	11	12	13	18
9	7	8	13	14	15	19	18		6	14	15	16	17	19

5	5	5	5	5		6	6	6	6	6
10	11	12	13	14		10	11	12	13	14
15	16	17	18	19		16	17	18	19	15

7	7	7	7	7	7		8	8	8	8	8
8	10	11	12	13	15		10	11	12	14	15
9	17	18	19	14	16		18	19	13	16	17

9	9	9	9	9
10	11	13	14	16
19	12	15	17	18

3.4 Completeness

If a system contains a statement which is expressible in the technical terms and relations of an axiom system and which cannot be proved to be true or false, the system obviously lacks a statement of axiom status, an independent statement. This was apparent in Axiom Set 3, when we found that it was not possible to prove *or* disprove certain statements. Recall that from Axiom Set 3 we could not prove either of the following: there exist at least eight points; there exist at most seven points. Yet one is true if and only if the other is false; hence, one must be true. This is not to suggest that one of these two statements should be adopted as an axiom but, rather, that when there are such statements that can be neither proved or disproved, the system lacks an independent statement and is incomplete according to the following definition:

Definition. An axiom system is *incomplete* if it is possible to add an independent axiom (phraseable in the system's technical vocabulary). If it is impossible to add such a statement, the system is *complete*.

We shall always assume that the independent axiom can be phrased in the system's technical vocabulary and that we need not repeat this requirement except for emphasis. If it were ignored, one would get such trivial situations as in Axiom Set 1, where the statement "All redheaded truck drivers are six feet tall," if added to that system, is an independent statement. We wish to avoid this.

We must now question whether it is in fact possible to find all of the independent statements of a system. Is it possible to prove or disprove every statement expressible within the vocabulary of the system? Is it possible to know when a system is complete? The definition is of little use, for how does one determine when the conditions of the definition have been met, namely, that all the possible independent statements phraseable in the system's terms have been discovered?

This problem is more tractable when approached in a slightly different way. Instead of looking at the system as an abstraction, one should consider some interpretation of it. Suppose, for example, one wishes to set up the axioms of Euclidean geometry. The problem is then specific: if one regards points and lines as undefined things, can one state a set of axioms from which the theorems implied will be those of Euclidean geometry alone and essentially different from any other geometry? Stated differently, can an abstract system be so completely characterized that it applies to essentially one and only one concrete interpretation, has, that is, an essentially unique model? If so, the system is said to be *categorical*.

In order to see how this approach supplies an answer to the problem, it is necessary to have a more precise definition of "categorical." To give such a definition, several new concepts must be introduced, concepts which in and of themselves are very useful in mathematics: *one-one correspondence* and *isomorphism*.

If the elements of two sets can be paired off in such a way that each element of one set occurs exactly once, matched with exactly one element of the other set, there is said to exist a *one-one correspondence* between the two sets.

If there exists a correspondence between two sets S_1 and S_2 such that every statement which is true when made about elements of S_1 is also true when made about the corresponding elements of S_2, the correspondence is said to *preserve relations*.

Definition. Two models of an axiomatic system are said to be *iso-morphic with respect to that system* if there exists at least one one-one correspondence between the elements of the system which preserves relations.

This concept is important enough to cover in more detail, rather than digress now, however, we shall postpone it until the next section, where we shall attempt to clarify it with several illustrations.

We are now able to state:

Definition. Whenever an axiomatic system is such that any two models are isomorphic, the system is said to be *categorical.*

And finally we can state the test:

Test: *If a system is categorical, then it is complete.*

To prove the statement in the test, suppose an axiomatic system is categorical but not complete. If not complete, then there exists a statement "A_n" such that it and "not-A_n" are consistent with the given set of axioms. Thus there exist models for the system $\{A_1, A_2, \cdots A_n\}$ and for $\{A_1, A_2, \cdots \text{not-}A_n\}$, hence showing that A_n is independent in the system. If it is now further supposed that the system is categorical, these two models must then be isomorphic; hence, corresponding statements in the two systems are either both true or both false. But this is impossible by the assumption that "A_n" is true in one and "not-A_n" is true in the other. This assumption must therefore be false; hence, if a system is categorical, it is complete.

In a preceding section it was seen that Axiom Set 3 is satisfied by every one of the models that satisfies Sets 1 and 2. As axioms were added the variety of interpretations decreased until, finally, when we included Axiom 6, we arrived at the System of Young, which is satisfied only by a model with nine points and twelve lines. Similarly, when we add Axiom 6 to Axiom Set 2 we get a system satisfied only by a model with seven points and seven lines. In these latter systems every two models satisfying one system are essentially the same; they are merely different symbols for the same things; they are, in a word, isomorphic. Hence, these last two systems are complete.

In conclusion, it should be pointed out that completeness is not only unessential but generally undesirable. One of the great advantages of an abstract axiomatic system is that in proving one theorem we are in effect proving many theorems. For every interpretation that satisfies the system, any theorem proved for the uninterpreted system becomes true in the interpreted system; therefore, the greater variety of models one can find for a system, the greater range of application it has. On the other hand, the "more" complete a system is, the fewer essentially different models one can find, the narrower is its range of applications. If one wishes to study one particular system intensively, completeness is useful; otherwise, it is not.

3.5 Examples of Isomorphisms

Consider Models I and II of Section 3.2

l: Sophomores:	Alan, Bob, Charley
m: Juniors:	Dick, Ernie, Fred
n: Seniors:	George, Herm, Irving
o: Algeria:	Alan, Dick, George
p: Bulgaria:	Bob, Ernie, Irving
q: Cambodia:	Charley, Fred, Herm
r: Dominican Republic:	Alan, Ernie, Herm
s: Egypt:	Bob, Fred, George
t: Finland:	Charley, Dick, Irving
u: Ghana:	Alan, Fred, Irving
v: Hungary:	Bob, Dick, Herm
w: India:	Charley, Ernie, George

l'	m'	n'	o'	p'	q'	r'	s'	t'	u'	v'	w'
1	4	1	1	1	2	2	2	3	3	3	7
2	5	4	5	6	4	5	6	4	5	6	8
3	6	9	7	8	7	8	9	8	9	7	9

As we know, the students are the "points" in one system and the numbers the "points" in the other. There are literally hundreds of ways in which a one-one correspondence between these two sets can be set up. Suppose we choose the following two:

(A)		(B)	
Alan	↔ 1	Alan	↔ 1
Bob	↔ 2	Bob	↔ 2
Charley	↔ 3	Charley	↔ 3
Dick	↔ 4	Dick	↔ 4
Ernie	↔ 5	Ernie	↔ 5
Fred	↔ 6	Fred	↔ 6
George	↔ 9	George	↔ 7
Herm	↔ 7	Herm	↔ 8
Irving	↔ 8	Irving	↔ 9

In order now to display an isomorphism, the "lines" must be corresponded in such a way that relations are preserved. For example, since Alan, Bob, and Charley belong to l, one must first of all be sure that there exists a line containing their "corresponding points," that is, that there exists a line containing 1, 2, and 3. These lines must then be made to correspond. Thus correspondence (A) is accompanied by the following:

$$(\text{A}')$$

$l \leftrightarrow l'$	$r \leftrightarrow o'$
$m \leftrightarrow m'$	$s \leftrightarrow s'$
$n \leftrightarrow w'$	$t \leftrightarrow t'$
$o \leftrightarrow n'$	$u \leftrightarrow p'$
$p \leftrightarrow r'$	$v \leftrightarrow q'$
$q \leftrightarrow v'$	$w \leftrightarrow u'$

Once the correspondence (A) has been determined, any change in (A') would cause the relation-preserving property to be lost. There is another way in which one can fail to preserve relations. Consider the correspondence given by (B). Because o contains Alan, Dick, and George, then by (B) there should exist a line containing 1, 4, and 7. But there is no such line in Model II; hence (B) fails to begin with. Of all the possible correspondences that can be set up between two models, there are usually many that preserve (all) relations (if the models are isomorphic), many that preserve some relations and, usually, some correspondences in which no relations are preserved. To show that there is an isomorphism, however, only one correspondence that preserves relations need be found.

EXERCISES 3.5

1. Suppose that the following is a model for Axiom Set 1 and set up a relation preserving one-one correspondence between it and Model II:

$$
\begin{array}{cccccccccccc}
1 & 1 & 1 & 1 & 2 & 2 & 2 & 3 & 3 & 3 & 4 & 5 \\
2 & 4 & 6 & 8 & 4 & 5 & 7 & 4 & 5 & 6 & 7 & 6 \\
3 & 5 & 7 & 9 & 6 & 8 & 9 & 9 & 7 & 8 & 8 & 9
\end{array}
$$

2. Set up a relation preserving one-one correspondence between:
(a) Model V and Model VI in Section 3.2.
(b) Model I and itself
(c) Model VII and itself

3. Can you find a one-one correspondence preserving *no* relations between:
(a) Model V and Model VI
(b) Model I and Model II

REVIEW EXERCISES

Answer true or false and explain or justify your answer.

1. A good test for consistency of a system is to derive all the theorems possible and, if no contradictions are uncovered, the system is consistent.

2. If two systems have the same number of elements they are isomorphic.

3. It is possible for a theorem to be implied by one axiomatic system and its contradictory by another axiomatic system.

4. In an axiomatic system completeness is always desirable.

5. In an axiomatic system independence is always desirable.

6. An inconsistent axiomatic system might imply a statement and its contradictory.

7. If an axiomatic system is satisfiable its model must be finite.

8. The test for independence involves consistency.

9. Completeness, independence, and consistency—as determined by the tests—all depend on the concept of satisfiability.

4 A Critique of Euclid

It may seem anachronistic to return to a discussion of Euclid at this point. It is an old saw in the rules of teaching that one should never teach mistakes, should not use errors or false statements as illustrations. But, while it is certainly not wise to reinforce errors by repeating them, let us counter one old saying with another: it is always possible to learn from past mistakes.

We are not returning to Euclid for the sole purpose of pointing out his mistakes. Rather, we hope to prepare the reader for what is to come in the following chapters.

The emphasis today on abstraction in mathematics sometimes causes mathematicians to overlook that simple understanding called intuition. When this happens, a brief look at the source of an idea may be helpful. We hope that such a study of the first book of the *Elements* will prepare the reader for the more abstract and abstruse approaches that begin in Chapter 5.

4.1 Tacit, or Unstated, Assumptions

In Chapter 1 we saw five statements that Euclid chose as axioms. In addition to these, he assumed some statements that he regarded as common notions, statements such as: things equal to the same thing are equal; equals subtracted from equals are equal; and so on. These statements, the axioms and the common notions, along with quite a few definitions, are listed at the beginning of the *Elements*.[1] From all of these

[1] See Appendix, pp. 217ff.

listed assumptions Euclid proceeded to prove over four hundred theorems of which only the first twenty-eight shall be of direct concern to us.[1] In studying the first twenty-eight theorems of the *Elements*, one finds that they more or less fall into two categories. There are those that may be regarded as theorems proper even in a system based on Hilbert's axioms. On the other hand, there are those that are merely proofs of the possibilities of certain constructions and proofs of existence via constructions. This second category, for the most part, will be of little use in the Hilbert system and we shall have no need to prove them as theorems.

The first three theorems of *Book 1* are of this latter type. Euclid justifies the construction of an equilateral triangle; he proves that one may mark off with a straightedge and collapsible compass a segment equal in length to a given segment; and, from a given point, draw a segment equal in length to a given segment. It is worthwhile to study these first three theorems. Not only do they have a certain literary charm, but they develop so nicely one after the other that they serve well as an introduction to the flavor of the work.

Present in the proofs of these three theorems are two *unstated* assumptions. This flaw of the *Elements* pervades the work. At times these assumptions are so subtly woven into the framework of the proofs that they pass unnoticed unless one knows exactly where to look; at other times they seem to have been introduced brazenly. In this instance they are of the first kind, and it is difficult indeed to discover on first reading what these unstated, or tacit, assumptions are. Consider Euclid's second theorem: (see Figure 4.1).

Theorem 2. To place at a given point (as an extremity) a straight line equal to a given straight line.
Proof: Let A be the given point, and BC the given straight line. Thus it is required to place at the given point A (as an extremity) a straight line equal to the given straight line BC.

From the point A to the point B let the straight line AB be joined (Post. 1); and on it let the equilateral triangle DAB be constructed. (Theorem 1).

Let the straight lines AE, BF be produced in a straight line DA, DB; (Post. 2); with center B and distance BC let the circle CGH be described; and again, with center D and distance DG let the circle GKL be described (Post. 3).

Then, since the point B is the center of the circle CGH, BC is equal to BG. Again, since D is the center of the circle GKL, DL is equal to DG. And in these DA is equal to DB; therefore, the remainder AL is equal to the remainder BG (C. N. 3).

But BC was also proved equal to BG; therefore, each of the straight lines AL, BC is equal to BG. And things which are equal to the same thing are also equal to one another; therefore, AL is also equal to BC (C. N. 1).

---

[1] See Appendix, p. 219.

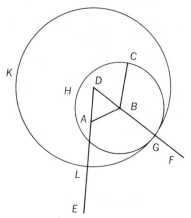

FIGURE 4.1

Therefore at the given point A the straight line AL is placed equal to the given straight line BC.

(Being) what it was required to do. ●

Can you find the flaw? Even a careful check of the proof of this theorem will show that all of the statements made in the proof actually follow from Euclid's axioms, common notions, definitions, or first theorem. The problem lies not in the statements *made* but in those that are *assumed but unstated*.

There are two such assumptions: that (under certain conditions) two circles intersect in two points and that, if a line passes through a point interior to a circle, it must intersect the circle (in two points).

In the circumstances given in the first three theorems there is not much doubt that these conditions hold true. But that is not the point. The criticism here is not that the assumptions are false; it is that the assumptions are not *stated*. If they are axioms, they should be stated as such; if they are theorems, they should be proven as such. But Euclid brings them in as hidden assumptions made credible by the diagrams. Nowhere does he make either an explicit assumption equivalent to these assumptions or one from which the truth of these statements would follow.

The rules must be such that this is not allowed in an axiomatic system. If a statement is not an axiom, definition, or theorem, it does not belong in a system. Here the solution is not difficult. One can introduce the statements themselves as axioms if one wishes or, better yet, can introduce a continuity axiom from which these statements would follow.

Hilbert chooses to introduce the Archimedean axiom to assure continuity of the lines and circles in his system. Stated rather intuitively, this axiom is:

Given two line segments, there exists an integral multiple of one which is greater than the other.

Another approach is to introduce the axiom of J. W. R. Dedekind (1831–1899), which states, more or less in Dedekind's own words:

If all points of a straight line fall into two classes, such that every point of the first class lies to the left of every point of the second class, then there exists one and only one point which produces this division of all points into two classes, this severing of the straight line into two portions.

We are going to refrain from introducing either of these axioms into our system because we feel that it is more important for the reader to see how many familiar theorems of ordinary plane geometry follow without an assumption of continuity. The main point is that if one wants continuity one must bring it in explicitly in some manner, not by unstated assumptions about diagrams. So agreed, let us turn to another problem.

In the proof of his famous fourth theorem, the *SAS* theorem, Euclid introduces for the first time the controversial method of *superposition*. It has been used and misused ever since and with much greater frequency than Euclid would have favored. Euclid himself does not use this technique very often but, evidently, saw no way to prove the fourth theorem without it.

There are various troubles involved in its use, all of which more or less boil down to the fact that in order to justify the use of superposition one must introduce such a statement as *figures remain unchanged when moved from one place to another.*

In fact, in the proof of the *SAS* theorem, Euclid brings in still another assumption; namely, that things which are equal may be made to coincide.

After years of controversy it was decided that it is impossible to use superposition without bringing in some axiom *justifying* superposition. Therefore, inasmuch as the use of superposition can be restricted to the proof of the *SAS* theorem, why not merely make that theorem an axiom? Such a course has been, and still is, often adopted.

To avoid this problem we shall, following Hilbert, introduce as an axiom a statement from which the *SAS* theorem readily follows without any such method as superposition. This involves introducing an undefined relation called *congruence*. This not only by-passes the need for superposition, it helps rid geometry of that much overused word "equals." Specifically, while Euclid will say that two triangles are *equal* if they coincide, he will also say that two triangles are *equal* if they have the same area (but perhaps cannot be made to coincide). There will be no discussion of area in this book; but, following Hilbert, we shall introduce the word "congruent" to replace the word "equal" as used in the first sense.

4.2 More Unstated Assumptions, Flaws, and Omissions

To show how many unstated assumptions Euclid introduces, and to illustrate other difficulties that arise in his system, let us examine and analyze the following elementary theorems from the *Elements:*

Theorem 5. In isosceles triangles the angles at the base are equal to one another; and, if the equal straight lines be produced further, the angles under the base will be equal to one another.
Proof: Let ABC be an isosceles triangle having the side AB equal to the side AC; and let the straight lines BD, CE be produced further in a straight line with AB, AC (Post. 2). I say that the angle ABC is equal to the angle ACB, and the angle CBD to the angle BCE.

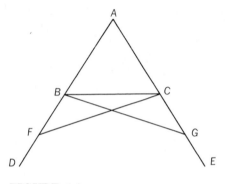

FIGURE 4.2

Let a point F be taken at random on BD; from AE the greater let AG be cut off equal to AF the less; and let the straight lines FC, GB be joined (Post. 1). Then, since AF is equal to AG and AB to AC, the two sides FA, AC are equal to the two sides GA, AB respectively; and they contain the common angle, the angle FAG. Therefore, the base FC is equal to the base GB, the triangle AFC is equal to the triangle AGB, and the remaining angles will be equal to the remaining angles respectively, namely, those which the equal sides subtend, that is, the angle ACF is equal to the angle ABG, and the angle AFC, to AGB (I.4).
And, since the whole AF is equal to the whole AG, and in these AB is equal to AC, the remainder BF is equal to the remainder CG.
But FC was also proved equal to GB; therefore, the two sides BF, FC are equal to the two sides CG, GB respectively; and the angle BFC is equal to the angle CGB, while the base BC is common to them; therefore, the triangle BFC is also equal to the triangle CGB, and the remaining angles will be equal to the remaining angles respectively; namely, those which the equal sides subtend. Therefore, the angle FBC is equal to the angle GCB and the angle BCF, to the angle CBG.

Accordingly, since the whole angle *ABG* was proved equal to the angle *ACF*, and in these the angle *CBG* is equal to the angle *BCF*, the remaining angle *ABC* is equal to the remaining angle *ACB*; and they are at the base of the triangle *ABC*. But the angle *FBC* was also proved equal to the angle *GCB*, and they are under the base. Therefore, et cetera . . .   Q.E.D.   ●

There are three preliminary questions one might ask about this proof:

1. Is it true that angle *BAC* = angle *FAC* = angle *GAB* = angle *FAG*?
2. Must angle *ABG* be larger than and wholly contain angle *CBG*? Must angle *ACF* be larger than and wholly contain angle *BCF*?
3. If Question 2 is satisfied, is it satisfied in such a manner that it follows that the "remaining angle *ABC* is equal to the remaining angle *ACB*"?

One should certainly want the answers to the above questions to be yes; indeed, there is something wrong if the answer is anything but yes. But this is irrelevant in an axiom system. The question once again is not whether these statements are true but, rather, *whether the statements follow from other statements explicitly assumed or proved.* Unfortunately, the answer is no. The statements are "taken" as true. From the diagrams it is apparent that they are true, but this does not constitute a proof. If not axioms, and if not proved, statements should not be part of the proof, diagram or not.

Another proof of this theorem is more likely to appear in high school texts. Given the triangle *ABC* with equal sides *AB* and *AC*, bisect angle *A*.

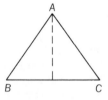

FIGURE 4.3

It follows easily from Theorem 4 that the two triangles are equal and hence that angles *B* and *C* are equal. As far as the *Elements*, and most high school texts, are concerned, this proof makes two unwarranted assumptions. It assumes that the bisector of an angle is unique and, furthermore, assumes that the bisector of an angle of a triangle intersects the opposite side. Euclid does not prove the former and ignores the latter, which he could not prove from his set of axioms even if he did consider it. Once again we emphasize that while these may be very obvious truths of geometry, the relevant question is whether or not they can be proved within the given system.

As another illustration of Euclid's rather easygoing introduction of unstated assumptions, consider the following theorem: (See Figure 4.4).

Theorem 6. If in a triangle two angles be equal to one another, the sides which subtend the equal angles will also be equal to one another.

Proof: Let ABC be a triangle having the angle ABC equal to the angle ACB; I say that the side AB is also equal to the side AC.

For, if AB is unequal to AC, one of them is greater.

Let AB be greater; and from AB the greater let DB be cut off equal to AC the less; let DC be joined.

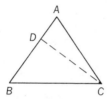

FIGURE 4.4

Then, since DB is equal to AC, and BC is common, the two sides DB, BC are equal to the two sides AC, CB respectively; and the angle DBC is equal to the angle ACB; therefore, the base DC is equal to the base AB, and the triangle DBC will be equal to the triangle ACB, the less to the greater; which is absurd.

Therefore, AB is not unequal to AC; it is therefore equal to it.

Therefore, et cetera . . . Q.E.D. ●

As in proofs throughout his work, Euclid is here assuming a trichotomy principle for segment lengths (later he will do the same for angle measure). In the third line of the proof he is assuming that given two segments AB and AC, either $AB = AC$; AB is less than AC; or AB is greater than AC, and exactly one of these conditions can hold.

In regard to the proof itself, it is apparently a proof by contradiction, but where exactly is the contradiction? He concludes that the "triangle DBC will be equal to the triangle ACB, the less to the greater, which is absurd." If he is not referring to *area*—and it is evident he is not—what can he mean when he says that "one triangle is less than another"? If there is a contradiction here (about triangles) it comes from the diagram, not from anything previously mentioned or proved in the system.

As a final illustration consider the following very important theorem (see Figure 4.5):

Theorem 16. In any triangle, if one of the sides be produced, the exterior angle is greater than either of the interior and opposite angles.

Proof: Let *ABC* be a triangle, and let one side of it *BC* be produced to *D*;
I say that the exterior angle *ACD* is greater than either of the interior and
opposite angles *CBA*, *BAC*.

Let *AC* be bisected at *E* (I.10) and let *BE* be joined and produced in a straight
line to *F*; let *EF* be made equal to *BE* (I.3), let *FC* be joined (Post. 1), and let *AC*
be drawn through to *G*(Post. 2).

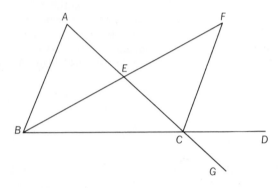

FIGURE 4.5

Then, since *AE* is equal to *EC*, and *BE* to *EF*, the two sides *AE*, *EB* are equal
to the two sides *CE*, *EF* respectively; and the angle *AEB* is equal to the angle
FEC, for they are vertical angles.

Therefore the base *AB* is equal to the base *FC*, and the triangle *ABE* is equal
to the triangle *CFE*, and the remaining angles are equal to the remaining angles
respectively, namely those which the equal sides subtend; (I.4).

Therefore the angle *BAE* is equal to the angle *ECF*. But the angle *ECD* is
greater than the angle *ECF*; therefore the angle *ACD* is greater than the angle
BAE.

Similarly also, if *BC* be bisected, the angle *BCG*, that is, the angle *ACD* (I.15),
can be proved greater than the angle *ABC* as well.

Therefore, et cetera . . .   Q.E.D.   ●

A short digression is in order here. When Euclid asserts in his Axiom 2
that a straight line can be produced indefinitely, this does not in itself
imply that straight lines are of infinite length. This point was ignored
until 1854 when B. Riemann proposed that a distinction be made between
a line being unbounded and a line being infinite in length.

As Euclid uses these terms, unboundedness is an *extent* concept; this
means, as in the second axiom, that a line may be extended indefinitely in
either direction. But unboundedness is compatible with the hypothesis
that a line is infinite in length as well as with the hypothesis that a line is
of finite length.

After this distinction was made there followed several new geometries in which straight lines are unbounded but not of infinite length; one such interpretation considers straight lines to be the great circles on the surface of a sphere. When "straight line" is so interpreted one gets geometries in which, while two points may determine a line, it may be that there are also an infinite number of lines through two points. Any two lines may enclose a space. This geometry is specifically "non-Euclidean" in the sense that there are no parallel lines whatsoever. Any of these considerations make for a *"non*-Euclidean" geometry.

Therefore, when Euclid tacitly assumes, in the proof of Theorem 16, that lines are of infinite length, the assumption is an important one to his geometry. Given the same proof for a triangle on a sphere it becomes invalid if *BF* is a semicircle, for then *F* falls on *BD* and angle *ACD* is equal to angle *ECF* and thus equal to angle *BAC*. And if *BF* is greater than a semicircle, angle *ACD* will be less than angle *BAC*. Thus, for a triangle on a sphere, not only does the proof fail but the "theorem" is a false statement; the theorems following from this one are false and there exists quite a different geometry. The geometry that does follow from the new assumptions is too complicated, unfortunately, to present here.

More relevant to this discussion is how Euclid knows, other than from looking at the diagram, that point *F* will fall in the interior of angle *ACD*. If a line is like a circle, it would be possible for *F* to fall between *B* and *E*. And even given that lines are of infinite length, how does one *prove* that *F* is in the interior of the angle so that it follows that angle *ACF* is less than angle *ACD*?

Euclid never defines or explicitly discusses such concepts as *interior* or *exterior*. He speaks again and again about one *side* or the other of a line but never defines what he means by a side of a line. And he ignores the concept of *betweenness*, so that whenever it is important to know that a point is between two others, or a ray is between two others (as when one wishes to say that one angle is less than another), he lets the diagram carry the weight of the argument.

In all these cases where Euclid tacitly introduces concepts by diagrams and uses diagrams to substantiate steps in a proof, he risks the chance of introducing not only false statements but self-contradictions. We shall try to show this now.

4.3   The Danger in Diagrams

Take a square each of whose sides is thirteen units and divide it into two rectangles of dimensions 8 by 13 and 5 by 13; then subdivide these into two congruent rectangular trapezoids whose parallel sides are 8 and 5 units long and into two congruent right triangles whose legs are 5 and 13 units long. Now rearrange these parts to form a rectangle. Finally, study Figure 4.6.

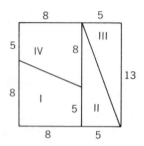
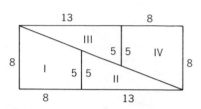

FIGURE 4.6

It can be seen more readily in the diagrams what is to be done than from the rather complicated set of directions preceding them. And this seems very simple until the following observation is made:

The area of the square is $13^2 = 169$ square units.

The area of the rectangle is $8 \times 21 = 168$ square units.

Obviously, something is wrong. It might help solve the dilemma to try this with different dimensions or with scissors and paper.

A more instructive illustration is the following well-known "paradox." We assume here that the reader has knowledge of the common elementary theorems of high school geometry.

All Triangles Are Isosceles

Given: Any triangle ABC

Construction: Construct the bisector of angle A and the perpendicular bisector of BC, the side opposite angle A.

Proof: Consider the following cases.

Case 1. The bisector of angle A and the perpendicular bisector of segment BC are either parallel or identical. In either case, the bisector of angle A is perpendicular to BC and hence, by definition, is an altitude. Therefore, the triangle is isosceles. (The conclusion follows from the Euclidean theorem: If an angle bisector and altitude from the same vertex of a triangle coincide, the triangle is isosceles.)

Suppose now that the bisector of an angle A and the perpendicular bisector of the side opposite are not parallel and do not coincide. Then they intersect in exactly one point, D. And there are three cases to consider:

Case 2. The point D is inside the triangle.

Case 3. The point D is on the triangle.

Case 4. The point D is outside the triangle.

For each case construct DE perpendicular to AB and DF perpendicular to AC, and in Cases 2 and 4 join D to B and D to C. In each case, the following proof now holds (see Figure 4.7):

$DE \cong DF$ because all points on an angle bisector are equidistant from the sides of the angle; $DA \cong DA$, and angle DEA and angle DFA are

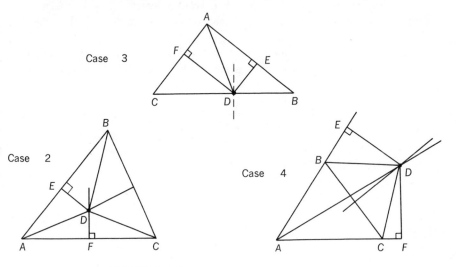

FIGURE 4.7

right angles; hence triangle ADE is congruent to triangle ADF by hypotenuse-leg theorem of Euclidean geometry. (We could also have used SAA theorem with $DA \cong DA$, and the bisected angle and right angles.) Therefore, we have $AF \cong AE$.

Now, $DB \cong DC$ because all points on the perpendicular bisector of a segment are equidistant from the ends of the segment. Also, $DE \cong DF$, and angles DEB and DFC are right angles. Hence triangle DEB is congruent to triangle DFC by hypotenuse-leg theorem. And hence $FC \cong BE$.

Therefore it follows that $AB \cong AC$—in Cases 2 and 3 by addition, in Case 4 by subtraction. Hence the triangle is isosceles.

To summarize the proof: It has been shown that if an angle bisector and the perpendicular bisector of the opposite side coincide or are parallel, the triangle is isosceles. It is known that if they neither coincide nor are parallel they must intersect in exactly one point which is either inside, on, or outside the triangle. But it has been shown that in every such case the triangle is isosceles. Therefore, every possible case has been considered and the theorem is proved.

Again, something is wrong. After a careful scrutiny, it will be obvious that not all cases have been considered. For while it is true that all locations of the intersection of the angle bisector and the perpendicular bisector of the opposite side have been considered, this has not been done for all locations of the points E and F. For example, in Cases 2 and 3, E and F might fall on the extension of AB and AC respectively, whereas in Case 4 E and F might fall *on* AB and AC respectively. It is left as an exercise to show that in these cases the proof still holds. Another possibility can easily be ruled out; namely, that E or F fall on a vertex of the triangle. But there are still other cases: the possibility that one of the points E or F might fall within a segment, while the other lies on an

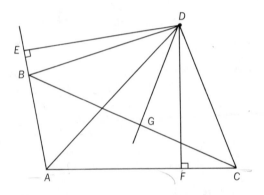

FIGURE 4.8

extension of its segment, has never been considered. Suppose this is done now: (See Figure 4.8).

Case 5. The same steps followed in Cases 1, 2, 3, and 4 may be repeated, but the results are not the same. For now it follows that $AB = AE - BE$ and $AC = AF + FC = AE + BE$ and since $AE - BE \neq AE + BE$, it follows that $AB \neq AC$. ●

It seems then that we have found the flaw in the reasoning: not every case had been considered. But, although this is true, has the flaw really been pointed out?

Most discussions of this paradox end at this stage. It has been shown that there are dangers in building an argument upon such weak foundations as diagrams; if that is all we were interested in showing, indeed we would be through with the problem. But there are broader aspects to the argument.

To appreciate fully the difficulties hidden here, let us approach the problem from a more logical perspective. In the proof of Case 1 a Euclidean theorem was cited. Its converse also holds; namely,

If a triangle is isosceles, then the angle bisector and the altitude from the same vertex coincide.

Thus the contrapositive must also hold; namely,

If the angle bisector and the altitude from the same vertex of a triangle do not coincide, the triangle is not isosceles.

The reader should not find it too difficult to prove that an angle bisector and altitude do not coincide if and only if the angle bisector and perpendicular bisector of the opposite side intersect in exactly one point. From this, it follows that *if the angle bisector and perpendicular bisector of the opposite side intersect in exactly one point, the triangle is not isosceles.*

But, it has just been proven by Cases 2, 3, and 4 that under the same hypotheses the triangle is isosceles.

This is a much more serious problem, one that is not answered by the mere existence of Case 5. In other words, it no longer suffices to show merely that Case 5 is a possible one; it must be shown, if no contradiction is to exist, that Cases 2, 3, and 4 are impossible.

This can be done as follows. It is a fact that the point *D* will always lie outside the triangle *ABC* and, of the two points *F* and *E*, one will always lie inside, the other outside the corresponding sides *AC* and *AB* of the triangle. For it can be proved that no line intersects all three sides of a triangle (unless one is extended) and it can be shown that the three points *G* (see Case 5), *E*, and *F* are collinear, so that one of the points *E* or *F* must lie on a side produced. If this were done, it would complete the argument and solve the "paradox."

What we wish to emphasize now is that any attempt to complete the above argument by the axioms and tools of Euclid's *Elements* will be hopeless. Not only does Euclid fail to present us with the tools, he does not even discuss such concepts as "between," "inside," or "outside." Within his system it is impossible to prove that a straight line cannot cut all three segments of a triangle. He must resort to argument from diagrams—and this, we should be more and more convinced, is a hazardous undertaking.

We can summarize some of the defects of the *Elements*, in particular those *tacit* or *unstated* assumptions which Euclid introduces into his work by means of diagrams or otherwise, as follows:

1. *continuity* of his figures
2. the *existence* of points and lines

3. *uniqueness* of certain points and lines

4. that a straight line which contains a vertex B and an interior point of a triangle ABC must also contain a point of the line segment AC

5. the existence of *order* relations on a line

6. the concepts of *inside* and *outside*

4.4   New Systems

To correct the defects listed in preceding sections, many axiom systems have been suggested and developed. Among these systems are those of Pasch——1882, Peano——1889, Hilbert——1899, Veblen——1904, and Birkhoff and Beatley——1940. Each is different; some have certain advantages over the others. Hilbert's system, perhaps because he is known as one of the outstanding mathematicians of the twentieth century, has had the most profound effect. Perhaps, too, this is because his system, as compared to the others, is most similar to Euclid's. Whatever the reasons, Hilbert's system has been so used, revised, and refined over the years that many variations of his system—changes in statements and phraseology—are now in existence. We shall use one such form as a basis, but shall incorporate many changes of our own.

Hopefully, the reader is prepared for this new approach to geometry. When we pause to prove something as obvious as the fact that a line has two "sides" or that a line "entering" a triangle must come "out," he will now be aware that it is not because we question the truth of these statements but that we wish to ascertain that they do indeed follow from the stated axioms.

Before we start, it should be made clear that we have specific objectives which require adopting the following restrictive procedures:

1. We shall introduce sufficient material to derive theorems related only to the first twenty-eight theorems of the *Elements*.

2. We shall refrain from introducing continuity considerations.

3. We shall not discuss any axioms needed for development of three dimensions, but shall, in effect, pretend that there are only two dimensions.

references

Dubnov, YA. S. *Mistakes in Geometric Proofs.* Translated by A. K. Henn and O. A. Titelbaum. Boston: D. C. Heath and Co., 1963.

Eves, Howard. *A Survey of Geometry,* vol. 1, chap. 8. Boston: Allyn and Bacon, Inc., 1963.

Fetisov, A. I. *Proof in Geometry*. Translated by T. M. Switz and L. Lange. Boston: D. C. Heath and Co., 1963.

Heath, T. L. *The Thirteen Books of Euclid's Elements*, 2d ed. New York: Cambridge University Press, 1926. Reprinted by Dover Publications, Inc., vol. 1., 1956.

Wilder, R. L. *Introduction to the Foundations of Mathematics*, chaps. 1 and 2. New York: John Wiley & Sons, Inc., 1952.

Young, J. W. *Lectures on Fundamental Concepts of Algebra and Geometry*, lectures IV & V. New York: The MacMillan Co., 1911.

part 2

An Axiomatic Development of Elementary Geometry

introduction

We are now going to begin the more formal part of the text, where more care will be taken about the manner in which we use words and introduce them. In the first part of the book we did not hesitate to talk about and use words and concepts not formally introduced. In Chapter 4, especially, we assumed that the reader had somewhere obtained a knowledge of many Euclidean theorems. This cannot be allowed in a formal axiomatic presentation.

As stated in Chapter 1, if we strip our vocabulary to

its essentials, we may categorize terms into two types: technical terms and universal language terms. The technical terms are the words *of the subject matter*. Some of them will be defined and some left undefined. The universal language terms are the words used *to talk about the subject matter;* almost all of these will be taken as undefined. Whenever we feel that a universal language term should be defined, we shall introduce its definition as a language rule rather than as a numbered definition. Under such circumstances, the distinction between a language rule and definition will all but disappear. We need not be concerned with such fine distinctions, which at best are introduced for neatness and clarity and are sometimes quite arbitrary.

Because we are more interested in clarification and instruction than in aesthetics and rigor, we shall make several compromises. It should be stated once and for all that we are not going to attempt to give a minimum set of axioms, or even to give an independent set of axioms. In choosing axioms and developing the system that follows, we hope to achieve four goals:

1. To show how the foundations of geometry (left to us by Euclid) must be propped up to permit us to prove even his elementary theorems.

2. To allow us to reach, in the quickest way, that body of theorems with which we are familiar from high school studies.

3. To gain a better understanding of the foundations of geometry.

4. To give us insight and understanding of the axiomatic approach to the study of mathematics in general.

Finally, when we are merely commenting upon a concept, axiom, or theorem we shall not hesitate to use common everyday language if it will aid our understanding or intuition.

5 The Foundations
of Geometry

5.1 Properties of Incidence and Existence

Language Rule 1: *"Point"* and *"line"* are UNDEFINED TECHNICAL terms.

The UNDEFINED UNIVERSAL LANGUAGE *terms will be the vocabulary of logic and sets, as well as those natural numbers needed.*

Notation Rule 1: *Any of the commonly accepted symbols of logic and sets may be used.*

Notation Rule 2: *Points will be denoted by* $A, B, C, \cdots, X, Y, Z$.

Axiom 0. Every line is a set of points.

Language Rule 2: *If a point* P *is an element of a line* m, *then one says variously:* m PASSES THROUGH P; m CONTAINS P; P is ON m; P LIES on m.

If a point P *is an element of more than one line, then one says the lines* MEET *in* P *or* INTERSECT *in* P.

Axiom 1. For any two given distinct points, there exists exactly one line containing them.

Axiom 2. Every line contains at least two distinct points.

Axiom 3. For any given line, there exists at least one point not on it.

Axiom 4. There exists at least one line.

While the undefined technical terms are never defined explicitly, they nevertheless are characterized by the axioms and thus have meaning given to them indirectly or implicitly.

Axiom 0 serves to clarify the relationship between the undefined terms. It is not a definition of "line" and cannot be considered one, because any "figure" of geometry will be a set of points. The axiom will help us to state exactly what we mean by different or distinct lines. For points, the word "distinct" is taken as one of the universal language terms; the same could be done for lines. However, because of its repeated use in theorems, we prefer to present it as a definition.

Definition 1. Two sets are the same iff they contain exactly the same elements. If two sets are not the same, they are called *distinct*.

It sometimes sounds awkward to state a definition in "iff" form; rather than force it, we introduce the following rule.

Language Rule 3: *Any definition whether so stated or not may be regarded as an "iff" statement.*

Definition 2. Any set, of at least two points, which is a subset of one line is called a *collinear* set. The elements of a collinear set are *collinear points*.

Proofs of the following theorems are left as exercises.

Theorem 1. There exist at least three points.

Theorem 2. There exist at least two distinct lines through any point.

Theorem 3. There exists at least one line not through a given point.

Theorem 4. Two distinct lines intersect in at most one point.

Language Rule 4: *Axiom 1 is usually expressed by saying a line is* DETERMINED *by two points.*

Notation Rule 3: *The line determined by two points A, B, will be denoted by:*

$$AB$$

also sometimes by small letters k, l, m.

Notation Rule 4: *Any time " = " is used, it will mean* IS IDENTICAL WITH. *Thus, " ≠ " means is* NOT IDENTICAL WITH.

Theorem 5. If C is on AB, and distinct from A and B then $CA = BC = AB$.

The following exercises will show how inadequate and incomplete this system is at this stage.

EXERCISES 5.1

1. Prove Theorem 1.
2. Prove Theorem 2.
3. Prove Theorem 3.

4. Prove Theorem 4.
5. Prove Theorem 5.

Two of the following exercises cannot be solved at this stage:

6. Prove that there exist at least four points.
7. Prove that there exist at least three lines.
8. Prove that there exist at least four lines.
9. Find a finite model for Axioms 0–4.
10. If $AB = AC$ and $B \neq C$, then $AB = BC$.

5.2 An Order Relation

It should be evident from the exercises just attempted that the axioms of incidence and existence given in section 5.1 are far from sufficient if one's purpose is to derive some of the standard theorems of Euclidean geometry. As yet, there are not enough axioms to derive more than three points on a line, let alone an infinite number. Not only is it impossible to generate an infinite number of points between any two points, we cannot even speak of a point "being between" two others. Not only are we unable to compare line segments as to which is greater or less, we cannot even speak of line segments. Strange as it may seem, each of these is dependent upon one relationship, which we shall call "between."

Euclid ignored this relationship in his axioms but introduced it by means of diagrams. In the last chapter it was seen that this can be a very treacherous procedure. This is not to say that we are going to try to do without diagrams; our intuitions and abilities to abstract are usually far too meager to allow us to do that. But we are going to try to keep from letting the diagrams become a part of a proof, a hidden way of introducing new and possibly fallacious material.

Language Rule 5: *"Between" is an undefined technical relation.*

Notation Rule 5: *"B is between A and C" will be denoted by:*

$$A*B*C$$

Even symbolism can be treacherous if one is not careful. We might have chosen to denote that "B is between A and C" by writing $B*A*C$ or $A*C*B$, and this would have been perfectly all right—less likely, in fact, to induce our intuitions to sneak in any spatial qualities or relations suggested by the arrangement of the letters. However, this is rather like saying, "Let B stand for swimming and S stand for bowling." It is unreasonable and confusing.

The axioms to be presented now, in a *modified* form, were first investigated by Pasch in the late nineteenth century and later adopted by Hilbert. They serve to give meaning to the undefined relation "between."

Axiom 5. $A*B*C$ iff $C*B*A$.

Axiom 6. If $A*B*C$, then A, B, C are distinct and collinear.

Axiom 7. If A, B, C are any distinct and collinear points, then exactly one of the following holds:

$$A*B*C, \qquad B*C*A, \qquad C*A*B$$

Observe that by Axiom 7 there are, for any three collinear points A, B, C, three possible orders: $A*B*C$, $B*C*A$, or $C*A*B$. Thus, for any four collinear points taken three at a time, there are the following twelve distinct possibilities:

$$A*B*C, \qquad A*B*D, \qquad A*C*D, \qquad B*C*D$$
$$A*C*B, \qquad A*D*B, \qquad B*D*C, \qquad A*D*C$$
$$C*A*B, \qquad D*A*C, \qquad D*B*C, \qquad D*A*B$$

Notation Rule 6: $A*B*C*D$ *is a shorthand for:* $A*B*C$ *and* $A*B*D$ *and* $A*C*D$ *and* $B*C*D$. *Analogous rules hold for more than four points.*

Axiom 8. If A, B, C, D are four distinct collinear points, and $A*B*C$, then exactly one of the following holds:

$$A*B*C*D, \qquad A*B*D*C, \qquad A*D*B*C, \qquad D*A*B*C$$

Axiom 9. If A and B are any two points, then
(a) there exists a point C such that $A*B*C$
(b) there exists a point D such that $A*D*B$
(c) there exists a point E such that $E*A*B$

Language Rule 6: *If* $A = B$, *then one may be* SUBSTITUTED *for the other, similarly if set* $X = $ *set* Y.

From Notation Rule 6 it follows that if $A*B*C*D$, then $A*B*D$ and $A*C*D$. What of the converse situation? If $A*B*C$ and $B*C*D$, does it

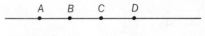

FIGURE 5.1

follow that B is between A and D or that C is between A and D? We certainly hope so. But this needs to be proved from the axioms. That it is "obvious" does not excuse it from the necessity of being proved. Unfortunately, sometimes the obviousness of the statement seems to be a barrier against proving it. This problem will come up frequently in the theorems and exercises to follow.

Theorem 6. If $A*B*C$ and $A*C*D$, then A, B, C, D are distinct and collinear.

Proof: By Axiom 6, A, B, C are distinct and collinear since $A*B*C$ is given. Likewise, A, C, D are distinct and collinear. If $B = D$, then by substitution $A*B*C$ and $A*C*B$, contradicting Axiom 7; hence, A, B, C, D are distinct. By Axiom 1, a unique line is determined by points A, C. Since B and D each belong to that line, A, B, C, D are collinear. ●

Theorem 7. If $A*B*C$ and $A*C*D$, then $A*B*C*D$.

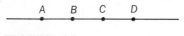

FIGURE 5.2

Proof: By Theorem 6, given $A*B*C$ and $A*C*D$, it follows that A, B, C, D are distinct and collinear. And since $A*B*C$, it follows by Axiom 8 that one of the following must hold: $A*B*C*D$, $A*B*D*C$, $A*D*B*C$, $D*A*B*C$. But from Axiom 7, if $A*C*D$, only $A*B*C*D$ can hold. (Why?) ●

Corollary: If A*B*C *and* A*C*D, *then* A*B*D *and* B*C*D.

The proofs of the following five theorems are left as exercises.

Theorem 8. If $A*B*D$ and $B*C*D$, then $A*B*C*D$.

Theorem 9. If $A*B*C$ and $B*C*D$, then $A*B*C*D$.

Theorem 10a. If $A*B*D$ and $A*C*D$ and $B \neq C$, then $A*B*C$ or $A*C*B$.

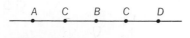

FIGURE 5.3

Theorem 10b. If $A*B*C$ and $A*B*D$ and $C \neq D$, then $B*C*D$ or $B*D*C$.

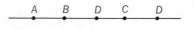

FIGURE 5.4

Theorem 10c. If $A*B*C$ and $A*B*D$ and $C \neq D$, then $A*C*D$ or $A*D*C$.

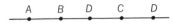

FIGURE 5.5

Definition 3: If a set S is the union of two (or more) nonempty subsets A_1, A_2 such that every element of S is an element of one and only one of the subsets, then A_1, A_2 are said to *form a partition* of S.

To say that every element of S is an element of one and only one of the subsets is the same as saying that the subsets are disjoint and that their union contains every element of S. Thus, $A_1 = \{1\}$, $A_2 = \{3, 5\}$, $A_3 = \{2, 4\}$ form a partition of the set $S = \{1, 2, 3, 4, 5\}$.

Definition 4. Let O be any point on a line m and A another point on m. Let S_1 be the set of all points on m consisting of A and all points X such that $O*X*A$ or $O*A*X$. Let S_2 be the set of all points X such that $X*O*A$. Then S_1, S_2 are called *half lines of line m with respect to O.*

Theorem 11. The half lines of line m with respect to O do not contain O.

Proof: Left as an exercise.

Definition 5. Let S_1, S_2 be two distinct nonempty disjoint sets which are disjoint from a set S. And let both of the following conditions hold:

(a) For any element A of S_1 and B of S_2, there exists a point of S between A and B;

(b) For any two elements A and B of the same set there does not exist a point of S between them;

then S is said to *separate S_1 and S_2.*

Theorem 12. Any point O on a line m separates m into two nonempty half lines which together with O form a partition of the line.

Proof: That the half lines are nonempty sets follows from Definition 4 and Axiom 9. (Why?) That there are exactly two half lines S_1 and S_2 and that they, together with O, form a partition of m follows from Axiom 7 and Theorem 11. (Why?)

Case 1. To show that O separates m into two half lines, let X_1 be any element of S_1 as given by Definition 4 and X_2 be any element of S_2 as given by the same definition; we must show X_1*O*X_2. By Definition 4 there are two possibilities. If $O*A*X_1$ and X_2*O*A, then from Axiom 5 it follows that X_1*A*O and $A*O*X_2$; then from Theorem 9 it follows that $X_1*A*O*X_2$ and hence X_1*O*X_2. If, on the other hand, $O*X_1*A$ and X_2*O*A, then by Axiom 5 $A*X_1*O$ and $A*O*X_2$; hence by Theorem 7 the conclusion follows.

Case 2a. Now, let X_1, Y_1 be any two distinct points of S_1 as given in Definition 4; then it is false that X_1*O*Y_1. There are three cases to consider: (1) if $O*X_1*A$ and $O*Y_1*A$, then it follows from Theorem 10a that $O*X_1*Y_1$ or $O*Y_1*X_1$. By Axiom 7 it cannot then be the case that X_1*O*Y_1; (2) similarly, using Theorem 10b, for $O*A*X_1$ and $O*A*Y_1$; (3) finally, suppose that $O*X_1*A$ and $O*A*Y_1$. Then by Theorem 7, $O*X_1*A*Y_1$ and hence $O*X_1*Y_1$. By Axiom 7 it is impossible that X_1*O*Y_1.

Case 2b. Now let X_2, Y_2 be any two distinct points of S_2 as given by Definition 4; then it is false that X_2*O*Y_2. For if X_2*O*A or Y_2*O*A, then by Axiom 5 it follows that $A*O*X_2$ and $A*O*Y_2$, and hence by Theorem 10b that $O*X_2*Y_2$ or $O*Y_2*X_2$, which by Axiom 7 is incompatible with X_2*O*Y_2.   ●

Language Rule 7: The sets S_1, S_2 in Definition 4 are said to be DETERMINED by O and A.

The next theorem establishes the uniqueness of half lines of line m with respect to O (independent of point A).

Theorem 13. Let O, A, A' be three points on a line m. The half lines with respect to O determined by O and A are the same as those determined by O and A'.

Proof: Left as an exercise.

Theorem 14. Let O, O' be distinct points on a line m. The half lines of m with respect to O are distinct from those with respect to O'.

Proof: Left as an exercise.

The maze of statements involved in such complex proofs often causes us to lose sight of our destination; we have an advantage, however, in knowing where we want to go. We are trying to build a Euclidean geometry from an axiomatic system. We know that we want points and lines to have certain properties. One such property is that a point should "divide" a line into two parts, where all points belonging to one part are on one side of the point and all points belonging to the other part are on the other side; it would be absurd for one point to belong to two parts, or for a point (other than the dividing point) not to be in either part. If we study the definitions and Theorem 12 ,we see that a point does "divide" a line in the sense our intuition says it should.

While we could easily choose some word to express everything expressed by the three definitions and Theorem 12, we shall refrain from doing so. One reason is that any word that would be relevant is likely to have another use in mathematics not necessarily consistent with ours. If nothing else, the failure to choose a single word emphasizes how deceptively complex such a simple question as "what does a point do to a line?" is.

EXERCISES 5.2

1. Prove Theorem 8. (Hint: Break it up into two parts similar to Theorems 6 and 7.)
2. Prove Theorem 9.
3. Prove Theorem 10a.
4. Prove Theorem 10b.
5. Prove Theorem 10c.
6. Prove Theorem 11.
*7. Prove Theorem 13.[1]
8. Prove Theorem 14.
9. Prove that if $A*B*C*D$, then A, B, C, D are distinct and collinear.
10. Prove that if $A*B*C*D*E$, then A, B, C, D, E are distinct and collinear.
11. Prove that there exist at least five *distinct* points on a line.
12. Prove that there exist at least five *distinct* points not on a line.
13. Prove that there exist at least three *distinct* points between any two points on a line.
*14. Prove that there exist at least five *distinct* points not on a line, no three of which are collinear.

5.3   Segments

Definition 6. Given two distinct points A and B, the set of all points X such that $A*X*B$ is called a *segment*.

Notation Rule 7: The set of all points X such that $A*X*B$ will be denoted by:

$$A-B$$

---

[1] An exercise preceded by * is considered to be more difficult and/or more significant than the others.

Theorem 15. A, B are not elements of $A-B$.

Proof: This follows immediately upon ruling out $A*A*B$ and $A*B*B$. ●

The proofs of the next four theorems are left as exercises. The proof of Theorem 19 may require more thought than the others.

Theorem 16. $A-B$ is not empty.

Theorem 17. $A-B = B-A$.

Theorem 18. $A-B$ is a subset of line AB.

Theorem 19. If $A-B = C-D$, then $C = A$ and $D = B$, or $C = B$ and $D = A$.

Once Definition 6 has been stated and these theorems proved, the following rule and definition make sense:

Language Rule 8: *A segment $A-B$ is* DETERMINED *by the points A, B.*

Definition 7. A, B are called the *endpoints* of segment $A-B$.

It should be noted that we are deviating from custom in not including the endpoints in the segment. This is an arbitrary decision. Over all, we shall find it a bit more convenient not to include the endpoints as part of the segment—thus we choose this way to state the definition.

We might also point out that our notation for a segment differs from the customary notation. While this notation is also arbitrary, it should be pointed out that it does not, in general, pay to change recognized symbols just to be different. We have chosen to use "A–B" instead of "$\overline{AB}$" for two reasons: segments have been defined as "open," that is, they do not include the endpoints; and we have not assumed that segments are continuous.

Theorem 20. Given $A-B$ and $A*P*B$, then $A-P$ and $P-B$ are subsets of $A-B$.

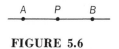

FIGURE 5.6

Proof: To show that $A-P$ is a subset of $A-B$ it must be shown that if $A*Y*P$, then $A*Y*B$. (Why?) Since it is given that $A*P*B$, it follows from Theorem 7 that $A*Y*P*B$ and, hence, $A*Y*B$. To show that $P-B$ is a subset of $A-B$, it must be shown that if $P*Y*B$, then $A*Y*B$. Since by Axiom 5 and hypothesis $B*Y*P$ and $B*P*A$, then by Theorem 7 $B*Y*P*A$ and, hence, $B*Y*A$. By Axiom 5 $A*Y*B$. ●

We shall certainly want a point on a segment to "divide" the segment into two parts. We can now prove a theorem analagous to Theorem 12.

Theorem 21. Any point P on a segment A–B separates A–B into two nonempty subsets A–P, P–B which together with P form a partition of A–B.

Proof: By Theorems 16 and 20 A–P, P–B are nonempty and subsets.

(a) Partition: Let P be any point on A–B and $X \neq P$ any point on A–B. We want to show that X is an element of one and only one of the subsets A–P, P–B. By Theorem 18 we are permitted to apply Axiom 8. By Axiom 8, if $A*P*B$ then $A*P*B*X$, $A*P*X*B$, $A*X*P*B$, or $X*A*P*B$. But since $A*X*B$ we have $A*P*X*B$ or $A*X*P*B$ but not both. Thus, for any point X either $P*X*B$ or $A*X*P$ but not both; hence, any point X of A–B is on one and only one of the sets A–P, P–B. Therefore, A–P, P–B together with P (Theorem 15) form a partition of A–B.

(b) Separation: Now let X_1, Y_1 be two distinct elements of set A–P. Then $A*X_1*P$ and $A*Y_1*P$. By Axiom 5 we may write $P*X_1*A$ and $P*Y_1*A$, from which it follows by Theorem 10a that $P*X_1*Y_1$ or $P*Y_1*X_1$; therefore it follows from Axiom 7 that X_1*P*Y_1 cannot hold. Similarly for X_2, Y_2 as elements of P–B.

Suppose now that X_1, X_2 are any two elements, one from each set; it follows from part (a) that they are distinct. We want to show that X_1*P*X_2. $A*X_1*P$ and $A*P*B$ imply $A*X_1*P*B$ and, hence X_1*P*B. X_1*P*B and $P*X_2*B$ imply X_1*P*X_2*B; hence X_1*P*X_2. ●

EXERCISES 5.3

1–5. Prove Theorems 15–19. (*Theorem 19)

*6. Prove that a segment has an infinite number of points. (Hint: by contradiction; if not, there must exist an empty segment.)

7. Prove that a line has an infinite number of points.

5.4 The Axiom of Pasch

In many standard proofs of high school geometry, lines through a vertex of a triangle are considered—angle bisectors, for example, as illustrated in Figure 5.7. In all such cases it is *assumed* that these lines intersect the opposite side of the triangle, but on what basis is such an assumption

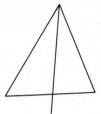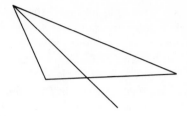

FIGURE 5.7

justified? Pasch, in the late nineteenth century, is credited with first maintaining not only that such a statement needs justification but that it is impossible to prove from the standard Euclidean axioms. So he introduced the following axiom, which is illustrated in Figure 5.8.

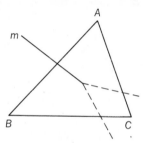

FIGURE 5.8

Axiom 10. (Pasch) If *A, B, C* are three distinct and noncollinear points, *m* is a line not passing through any of them, and *m* contains a point of segment *A–B*, then *m* also contains a point of segment *A–C* or *B–C*.

This axiom does not immediately solve the problem about angle bisectors; before we can solve such a problem we must first be able to state it precisely. Note, as in Figure 5.9, that not every line through a

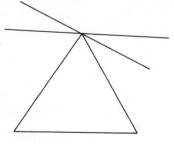

FIGURE 5.9

vertex of a triangle passes through the opposite side; it must also pass through a point *inside* the triangle.

In order to express and prove such a theorem we shall want definitions of "triangle" and "inside," as well as some related theorems. Thus we shall postpone some of this until we have established the groundwork. Let us start with a theorem that shows that the alternative expressed in Pasch's axiom is an exclusive one. See Figure 5.10.

Theorem 22. If A, B, C are noncollinear points, any line m containing a point of segment A–B, and a point of segment A–C, cannot contain a point of segment B–C.

Proof: Suppose that there exists a line m with three such points; that is, a line with points D, E, and F such that D belongs to A–B, E belongs to

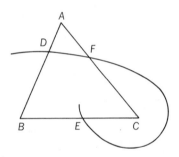

FIGURE 5.10

B–C, and F belongs to A–C. By Axiom 7 one point, say F on A–C must lie between the others, so $D*F*E$. Since E is contained in B–C, it is contained in line BC—this follows from Theorem 18. Similarly, D is contained in line AB. It follows, therefore, that D, E, and B are noncollinear, for otherwise Theorem 4 is contradicted. (Why)? Thus by Axiom 10 the line AC which intersects D–E at F must intersect either B–E or B–D. But by Theorem 4 and Axiom 7 this is impossible. Hence, the assumption is false. The argument proceeds similarly if $D*E*F$ or $F*D*E$. ●

We might have introduced the following definition at the beginning of the section. By postponing it until now, we have shown merely that this definition is unnecessary; we now hope to show that it helps us to make statements more succinctly, clearly, and in keeping with our intuition.

Definition 8. Given three distinct noncollinear points A, B, C, the new set which is the union of A, B, C together with A–B, A–C, and B–C, is called a *triangle*, and:

A, B, C are called the *vertices;* each one a *vertex.*

A–B, A–C, B–C are called the *sides.*

The lines containing the sides are called the *sidelines.*

Because of Theorems 17 and 19 and the above definition we may state the following rules:

Language Rule 9: *A triangle is* DETERMINED *by its vertices.*

Notation Rule 8: *The triangle determined by A, B, C will be denoted by:*

$$\triangle ABC$$

We shall read this and often denote it "triangle ABC."

It should be noted that because endpoints are not parts of segments, vertices are not parts of sides of triangles.

We may now state Axiom 10 in the simpler form:

If a line not through a vertex intersects one side of a triangle, it intersects at least one of the other sides.

Theorem 22 may be restated in either of the following more intuitive forms:

If a line intersects one side of a triangle, it intersects at most one of the other sides.

A line cannot intersect all three sides of a triangle.

The machinery has now been built to enable us to prove a very important theorem. But first we shall want a definition and two preliminary theorems:

Definition 9. Let m be any line and P a point not on it. Let S_1 be the set of all points consisting of P and all points X not on m such that P–X contains no point of m. Let S_2 be the set of all points Y, such that P–Y contains a point of m. Then S_1, S_2 are called *half planes of line m.*

Theorem 23. Half planes of a line m are nonempty.

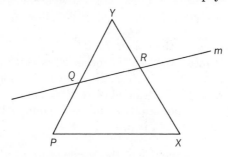

FIGURE 5.11

Proof: Given a line m, there exists a point P not on m and a point Q on m. There exists a point Y such that $P*Q*Y$ and, hence, $P-Y$ contains a point of m. There exists another point R on m and a point X such that $Y*R*X$. Then by Theorem 22 m cannot contain a point of $P-X$. ●

Theorem 24. There exist exactly two half planes of a line m (relative to a point P) which together with m form a partition of the set of all points.

Proof: Every point is either on m or not. No point is both. Consider the points not on m. By the argument of Theorem 23, if M is a point of m, then there exist points P, Q not on m and such that $P*M*Q$. Let X be any point not on m. If X is collinear with P and Q, then exactly one of the following holds: $X*P*Q$, $P*X*Q$, $P*Q*X$, $X = P$ or $X = Q$. Then exactly one of the segments $Q-X$, $P-X$ meets m. (Proof in the first three cases is nontrivial and is left as an exercise.) If X is not collinear with P and Q, then once again exactly one of the segments $Q-X$, $P-X$ meets m.

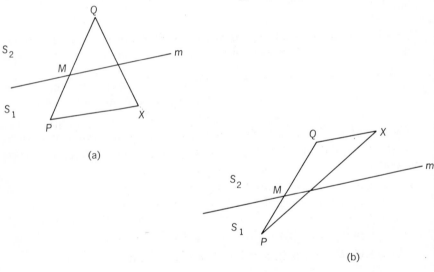

FIGURE 5.12

For if neither meets m, then since $P*M*Q$, Axiom 10 is contradicted. If both $P-X$, $Q-X$ meet m, then Theorem 22 is contradicted. Thus, if $P-X$ does not meet m, X is in S_1 as given in Definition 9; and if $Q-X$ does not meet m, then $P-X$ does and X is in S_2 as given in Definition 9. Since these are the only possibilities and each point is in exactly one of the sets m, S_1, S_2 the theorem is proved. ●

It is now possible to prove one of the basic theorems of the foundations of Euclidean geometry. It is often assumed as an axiom (in place of

Pasch's) and called *The Plane Separation Postulate:* any line separates the set of all points into two half planes. To understand the proof, however, it may be necessary to review the meaning of "separates."

Definition 5 is stated in terms of any set S separating two others, S_1 and S_2. S_1 and S_2 must be distinct nonempty disjoint sets which are disjoint from S and are such that two conditions hold: if A is an element of S_1 and B is an element of S_2 there exists a point of S between them; conversely, if there exists a point of S between A and B, they must belong to distinct sets. The converse, if stated in contrapositive form, says: if A and B belong to the same set, there does not exist a point of S between them.

Theorems 23 and 24 show that half planes of a line m, together with m, satisfy the properties of S_1, S_2, and S of the definition. It must now be shown that they satisfy case (a) and case (b) of Definition 5.

Theorem 25. Any line m *separates* the set of all points into two half planes.

Proof: By Theorems 23 and 24 we know that the half planes are non-empty sets disjoint from each other and m. Let P be a point of one half plane, and let A, A' be any two points not on m such that A–P, A'–P contain no point of m. Let B, B' be any two points of the other half plane; that is, not on m but such that P–B, P–B' do contain a point of m.

Case a. If any 3, 4, or 5 of the points P, A, A', B', B are collinear, then it follows that m intersects A–B, A'–B', A'–B, A–B'. (Proof left as an exercise.) If no three of the points are collinear, then it follows directly from Axiom 10 that m intersects A–B, A'–B', A'–B, A–B'.

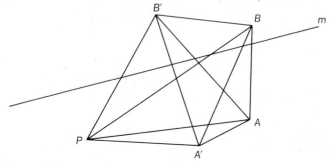

FIGURE 5.13

Case b. The converse says that if A–B intersects m, then A, B belong to different half planes of m. In its contrapositive form, this says that if A, A' belong to the same set, then A–A' does not intersect m. If either A, P, A' are collinear, or B, P, B' are collinear, then it follows that neither

$A-A'$ nor $B-B'$ intersect m. (Proof left as an exercise.) If A, P, A' are not collinear, then since by hypothesis neither $P-A$ nor $P-A'$ intersect m, it follows that Axiom 10 would be contradicted if m intersected $A-A'$. If B, P, B' are not collinear, then since by hypothesis $P-B$ and $P-B'$ each intersect m, by Theorem 22 m does not intersect $B-B'$.   ●

Language Rule 10: *The sets S_1, S_2 in Definition 9 are said to be* DETER-MINED BY m AND P.

The following theorem establishes the uniqueness of half planes determined by a line m and any point not on it.

Theorem 26. Let m be a line, P, P' two points not on m. The half planes determined by m, P are the same as those determined by m and P'.

Proof: Left as an exercise.

Theorem 27. Let m, m' be distinct lines. The half planes of line m are distinct from the half planes of line m'.

Proof: Left as an exercise.

EXERCISES 5.4

1. Complete Theorem 24.
2. Complete Theorem 25.
*3. Prove Theorem 26.
4. Prove Theorem 27.
5. Prove that if $A*F*B$, and $B*C*D$, then there exists a point E on $F-D$ such that $A*E*C$. A, B, C are noncollinear.
6. Prove that if A, B, C are three distinct noncollinear points and D, E points such that $B*C*D$, and $C*E*A$, then there exists a point F on line DE such that $A*F*B$.
7. In exercise 6, show that $D*E*F$.
*8. If in a $\triangle ABC$, $A*D*B$, $A*E*C$, and $B*F*C$, then $A-F$ meets $D-E$.
9. Prove that in $\triangle ABC$, if $A*D*B$, $B*E*C$, then $A-E$ and $C-D$ intersect.

5.5   Convex Sets

Definition 10. A set S is called a *convex set* if and only if for any two points P, Q, belonging to S, the entire segment $P-Q$ is contained in S.

Theorem 28.

(a) Every line is a convex set.
(b) Each half line of a point O is a convex set.

Proof: (a) That every line is a convex set follows immediately from the definition of convex, the definition of segment, and Axiom 6.

(b) To show that each half line is a convex set, it must be shown that if X_1, Y_1 are any two elements of the same half line and X is any point such that X_1*X*Y_1, then X is an element of the same half line. Thus, given X_1*X*Y_1, the following four relations must be shown:

(1) If $O*X_1*A$, $O*Y_1*A$, then $O*X*A$
(2) If $O*A*X_1$, $O*A*Y_1$, then $O*A*X$
(3) If $O*X_1*A$, $O*A*Y_1$, then $O*X*A$ or $O*A*X$
(4) If X_1*O*A, Y_1*O*A, then $X*O*A$

Proofs of these are left as exercises. ●

Theorem 29. Every segment is a convex set.

Proof: Left as an exercise.

Theorem 30. Each half plane of a line m is a convex set.

Proof: It must be shown that:

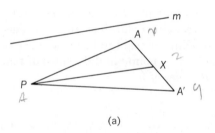

(a)

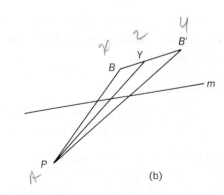

(b)

FIGURE 5.14

Y   G

(a) If A, A' are points such that $P-A$, $P-A'$ do not contain a point of m and X is a point such that $A*X*A'$, then $P-X$ does not contain a point of m.

(b) If B, B' are points such that $P-B$, $P-B'$ contain a point of m and Y is a point such that $B*Y*B'$, then $P-Y$ contains a point of m. Left as an exercise.   ●

Theorem 31. The intersection of n convex sets is a convex set. (n is a natural number.)

Proof: Left as an exercise. (We shall not need this theorem for n greater than 4.)

Definition 11. The two half lines of a point O whose existence and properties are given by preceding definitions and theorems are called the two *sides of O* on line m. Two points in the same half line are said to be *on the same side of O;* two points in different half lines are said to be *on opposite sides of O.*

Definition 12. The two half planes of a line m whose existence and properties are given by preceding definitions and theorems are called the two *sides* of line m. Two points are said to be *on the same side of m* if they are in the same half plane; two points in different half planes of a line m are said to be *on opposite sides of m.*

If we translate the content of preceding theorems into the language of Definition 12, we find that we have already proved the following theorem, listed here for future reference. (See Figure 5.15.)

Theorem 32.

(a) If A, B are on opposite sides of m, and B, C are on the same side, then A, C are on opposite sides.

(b) If A, B are on opposite sides of m, and B, C are on opposite sides of m, then A, C are on the same side of m.

(c) If A, B are on the same side of m, and B, C are on the same side of m, then A, C are on the same side of m.

Definition 13. The set of all points on a line, on the same side of a point O, is called a *ray; O* is called the *terminal* or *endpoint.* The two rays corresponding to the two sides of a point O are called *opposite rays.*

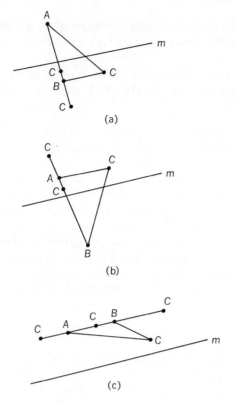

FIGURE 5.15

If we translate the content of preceding theorems into the language of Definition 13, we find that we have already proved most of the following theorem. Again, we list it here for future reference; proof of part (g) is left as an exercise.

Theorem 33.

(a) A ray is a convex set.
(b) A ray is a subset of a line.
(c) A ray has a unique endpoint.
(d) The endpoint is not a part of a ray.
(e) There exist unique opposite rays.
(f) A ray is determined by its endpoint and any one of its points.
(g) A ray with endpoint on a line, but not lying on the line, has all of its points on the same side of the line.

Notation Rule 9: A ray determined by endpoint A and point B on the ray will be denoted by:

$$\overrightarrow{AB}$$

We shall read this and often denote it, "ray AB."

The manner in which we have introduced rays is not the customary one. Concerning the notation, we might argue for the introduction of a new symbol as we did in the case of segments; however, it is hoped that the symbol for "segment" has served its purpose well enough that no further proliferation of symbols is needed. More important, perhaps, is a needless proliferation of *terms*, the introduction of both "half lines" and "rays." Either one of the two terms might have sufficed, but it is instructive, we feel, to introduce a "barren" term first, to derive its properties, and then to introduce a ray as something having those properties.

EXERCISES 5.5

1. Prove Theorem 28.
2. Prove Theorem 29.
3. Prove Theorem 30. (Be sure to consider the cases of collinearity.)
4. Prove Theorem 31.
5. Prove part (g) of Theorem 33.

5.6   Interior and Exterior

Definition 14. The *interior* of a triangle with vertices A, B, C is the set of all points which is the intersection of:
(a) The side of the line AB containing point C.
(b) The side of the line BC containing point A.
(c) The side of the line AC containing point B.
The *exterior* of a triangle is the set of all points which are neither on the triangle, nor in its interior.

Theorem 34. The interior of a triangle is convex.

Proof: Left as an exercise.

Theorem 35. If P, Q are points on two sides of a triangle, and R is a point on line PQ and in the interior of the triangle, then $P*R*Q$.

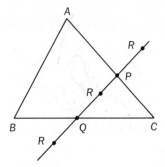

FIGURE 5.16

Proof: By Axiom 7 one of the three orders, $P*Q*R$, $Q*P*R$, $P*R*Q$, holds. Suppose that $P*Q*R$ holds where P is on A–C, Q is on B–C. Then P and R are on different sides of line BC. By Theorem 33 (g) every point of ray CA is on the same side of line BC. In particular, points P and A are on the same side of line BC. Hence, by Theorem 32 (a) A and R are on opposite sides of line BC, contradicting the assumption that R is an interior point of the triangle. Similar argument rules out $Q*P*R$. Hence, $P*R*Q$.   ●

Theorem 36. If P, Q are points on two sides of a triangle, and R is a point such that $P*R*Q$, then R is in the interior.

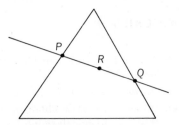

FIGURE 5.17

Proof: Left as an exercise.

Theorem 37. The interior of a triangle is nonempty.

Proof: Left as an exercise.

Theorem 38. In any triangle ABC, if $A*D*B$, then C–D together with the interiors of triangle ACD, and CDB form a partition of the interior of triangle ABC.

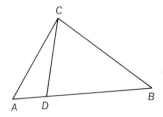

FIGURE 5.18

Proof: Left as an exercise.

We come at last to the "obvious" theorem mentioned a few sections back, that if a line passes through a vertex A of a triangle, and an interior point, it must cut the opposite side. Our intuition cries out, "what else can it do?" Look at the diagram of a triangle. A line through A and a point

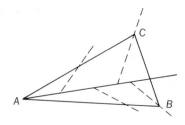

FIGURE 5.19

interior to a triangle ABC cannot possibly cut back through $A–C$, $A–B$, B or C; therefore, it must cut $B–C$.

The trouble with this "proof" is that we have surreptitiously argued from the diagram. Segments, as we draw them, are continuous. But we have said nothing so far that would justify such an assumption. How do we know that there is not a gap or hole in one of the segments of the triangle which would permit the line to "get outside" the triangle without having another point in common with lines AC or AB or having any point in common with $B–C$? Even if we introduce continuity, this merely fortifies our intuition. It must still be *proven* that a line through A crosses line BC and, furthermore, that it does so between B and C. We have seen before that sometimes the most obvious of theorems are difficult to prove, but we are finally in a position to give a not-so-simple proof of this very simple theorem.

In order to make it easier to state the theorem, we introduce the next definition.

Definition 15. In any triangle, the side that does not have a particular vertex as endpoint is called the *side opposite* that vertex. The vertex is the *opposite vertex*.

Theorem 39. A line through a vertex and a point interior to a triangle intersects the side opposite the vertex.

Proof: If a line m passes through vertex A of triangle ABC, then it intersects both lines AB and AC; so by Theorem 4 it cannot do so again. Suppose that m passes through interior point P. Take any point Q on $A\text{–}C$. Then by Axiom 10, if line QP does not contain a vertex, it intersects $A\text{–}B$ or $B\text{–}C$.

Case 1. Suppose that line QP intersects $A\text{–}B$ in R; then by Theorem 35 $Q*P*R$. In triangle QRC, since $Q*P*R$, Pasch's Axiom holds, and line AP,

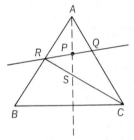

FIGURE 5.20

since it cannot intersect line AC again, must intersect $R\text{–}C$ in some point S. Thus $R*S*C$. And, once again, in triangle RBC Pasch's Axiom holds, and since line AS cannot intersect line AB again, it must cut $B\text{–}C$.

Case 2. Suppose line QP intersects $B\text{–}C$ in a point T. Then by Theorem 35 $Q*P*T$ and, once again, Pasch's Axiom holds in triangle QTC. Since AP cannot intersect line AC again, it must intersect $T\text{–}C$ and, hence, $B\text{–}C$.

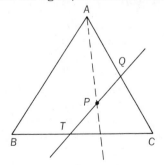

FIGURE 5.21

Case 3. Suppose now that line QP contains a vertex; it cannot contain A or C. Hence, it contains B. (It is left as an exercise to show that $Q*P*B$.) Using triangle QBC, by similar argument to the above, it follows that line AP intersects B–C. •

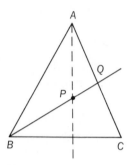

FIGURE 5.22

The next theorem is introduced primarily because, although it too is obvious, its equally obvious analogue on angles, which can be stated in the next section, cannot be proved unless a new axiom were to be added.

Theorem 40. Any line through an interior point of a triangle, but not containing a vertex of the triangle, meets at least one of the sides.

Proof: Let P be an interior point of a triangle ABC, and let m be a line through P. Take any point on a side, say Q on A–C; if m contains Q the conclusion follows. If m does not contain Q, then consider a line QP. By Axiom 10, if line QP does not contain B, it intersects either A–B or B–C. If line QP intersects A–B in a point, say R, then a triangle ARQ is formed; if QP intersects B–C in a point, say S, then triangle QSC is formed. It follows from Theorem 35 that in one case $Q*P*R$, and in the

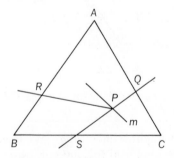

FIGURE 5.23

other Q^*P^*S. Hence, in either case, Axiom 10 applies, and m intersects either A–R or A–Q in triangle ARQ, or S–C or Q–C in triangle QBC. Hence, in either case, one of the sides of triangle ABC is met. Finally, if line QP contains B then Q^*P^*B (see exercise 5, Exercises 5.6) and the conclusion follows. ●

EXERCISES 5.6

1. Prove Theorem 34.
2. Prove Theorem 36.
3. Prove Theorem 37.
*4. Prove Theorem 38.
5. Complete the proof of case 3 of Theorem 39.
6. Prove that if a line passes through a point interior to a triangle and a point on a side of the triangle, and does not pass through one of the other sides, then it must pass through the opposite vertex.
7. Prove that in a triangle ABC if A^*D^*B, B^*E^*C, then the point of intersection of A–E and C–D is in the interior of the triangle.
8. Prove that a point is in the interior of a triangle if and only if it is between a vertex and a point of the opposite side.

5.7 About Angles and Rays

Definition 16. Given two distinct noncollinear rays, say ray AB and ray AC with common terminal point A, the union of the two rays together with the terminal point is called an *angle*. The rays are the *sides* of the angle. The lines containing the sides are the *sidelines*.

The terminal point is called the *vertex*.

Notation Rule 10. An angle which is the union of rays AB and AC will be denoted by:

$$\angle CAB \qquad or \qquad \angle BAC$$

or, where no ambiguity exists, simply by:

$$\angle A$$

We shall read these and often denote them: "angle CAB," "angle BAC," "angle A."

This definition of angle might seem strange. We have chosen it because it is sufficient and most economical for our purposes. It could be argued with justification that even for our purposes it would have been well to include a "straight angle" as an angle. For even though we are always in command in choosing definitions, we should have some reason for including, deleting, or altering concepts. What have we gained or lost by this definition?

We have gained the following: any angle has a unique interior; any angle has a unique vertex; we have adhered to the original Euclidean concept of angle; and, although we are not considering three dimensions, it would be useful in that case, too, in that an angle determines a unique plane.

In proving one theorem later we shall find that it would have been useful to be able to speak of a "straight angle"; we may consider that alternative at that time. For now, Definition 16 is more useful.

The next theorem is often tacitly assumed.

Theorem 41. Given noncollinear rays $\overrightarrow{AB}$, $\overrightarrow{AC}$ with B' on $\overrightarrow{AB}$ and C' on $\overrightarrow{AC}$, $\angle BAC = \angle BAC' = \angle B'AC = \angle B'AC'$.

Proof: Follows from Definition 16 and Theorem 33, part (f).   ●

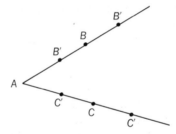

FIGURE 5.24

Of the many linguistic shortcuts in mathematics, some are most unfortunate. There are also many times that a word is used in a variety of ways, each way involving a different concept or meaning. We have already used the word "side," for example, to refer to part of a triangle, part of an angle, and to one of the half planes into which a line separates and partitions the set of all points. While so many uses may be confusing, it would be more confusing to try to change a usage so universally practiced.

One unfortunate shortcut is the common practice of referring to the "area of a triangle," even though it is obvious that a triangle can have no area. Because it is so obvious, we can however, perhaps excuse this usage as harmless. Another example more relevant here is the practice of speaking of a "side" of a ray or of a segment. In either case, we are obviously referring to one of the two sides into which the line containing the ray or segment, that is, the sideline, separates the set of all points.

Still another common use—and misuse—of a word is the standard practice of referring to the angles of a triangle. Strictly speaking, a triangle does not contain an angle. It cannot. For the sides of a triangle are segments, whereas the sides of an angle are made up of rays. Nevertheless, we shall continue to use such words and phrases according to the following rules:

Language Rule 11: *A* SIDE OF A SEGMENT *or* SIDE OF A RAY *refers to a side determined by the sideline of which the segment or ray is a subset.*

An ANGLE OF A TRIANGLE *refers to the angle which has a vertex of a triangle as vertex and two triangle segments with that vertex as endpoint as subsets.*

A SIDE OPPOSITE AN ANGLE *refers to that segment of a triangle which does not have the vertex of the angle referred to as an endpoint. That is, the side opposite angle BAC is the same as the side opposite vertex A. Similarly, for* ANGLE OPPOSITE A SIDE.

Definition 17. The *interior of an angle CAB* is the intersection of the side of the ray *AC* that contains *B*, and the side of the ray *AB* that contains *C*.

The *exterior of an angle* is the set of all points which are not in the interior or not on the angle.

Theorem 42. An angle has exactly one vertex and exactly one interior.

Proof: Left as an exercise.

Theorem 43. The interior of an angle is nonempty.

Proof: Left as an exercise.

Theorem 44. The interior of an angle is a convex set.

Proof: Left as an exercise.

Theorem 45. If a point *D* lies in the interior of an angle *BAC*, then every point of the ray *AD* lies in the interior.

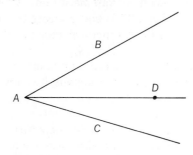

FIGURE 5.25

Proof: Left as an exercise.

Theorem 46. If P, Q are points on two sides of an angle, and R is a point on line PQ and in the interior of the angle, then $P*R*Q$.

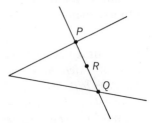

FIGURE 5.26

Proof: Left as an exercise.

Theorem 47. If P, Q are points on two sides of an angle, and R is a point such that $P*R*Q$, then R is an interior point of the angle.

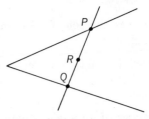

FIGURE 5.27

Proof: Left as an exercise.

Theorems 46 and 47 are analogues of Theorems 35 and 36; we have already indicated that there is no analogue, for angles, for Theorem 40. To be more specific, it cannot be proved in this text that any line through an interior point of an angle, but not containing a vertex of the angle, cuts one of the sides. That such a statement cannot be proved is rather amazing; it seems so obvious. The reader might try for himself to figure out what axiom must be added to make such a proof possible. If he does not succeed, the following hint might help: an axiom will be introduced in Chapter 9 which is, in effect, a disproof or counterexample.

The following theorems and definition will be referred to in succeeding sections:

Theorem 48. If D is an interior point of $\angle BAC$, then $\overrightarrow{AD}$ intersects B–C. (This is sometimes called the *Crossbar* theorem.)

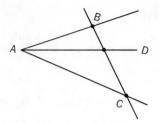

FIGURE 5.28

Proof: Left as an exercise.

Theorem 49. If D is an interior point of angle BAC and E is any exterior point, then segment D–E contains a point of the angle.

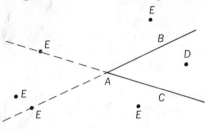

FIGURE 5.29

Proof: Left as an exercise. (*Hint:* the diagram indicates cases to be considered.)

Definition 18. Given an angle BAC formed by $\overrightarrow{AB}$ and $\overrightarrow{AC}$, then $\overrightarrow{AD}$ is *between* $\overrightarrow{AB}$ and $\overrightarrow{AC}$ iff $\overrightarrow{AD}$ is in the interior of angle BAC.

Theorem 50. A ray $\overrightarrow{AD}$ is between two others, $\overrightarrow{AB}$ and $\overrightarrow{AC}$, iff there exist points B', D', C' on $\overrightarrow{AB}$, $\overrightarrow{AD}$, $\overrightarrow{AC}$, respectively, such that $B'*D'*C'$.

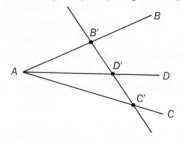

FIGURE 5.30

Proof: Left as an exercise.

Theorem 51a. If $\overrightarrow{AD}$ is between $\overrightarrow{AB}$ and $\overrightarrow{AC}$, and if $\overrightarrow{AE}$ is between $\overrightarrow{AD}$ and $\overrightarrow{AC}$, then $\overrightarrow{AE}$ is between $\overrightarrow{AB}$ and $\overrightarrow{AC}$.

Theorem 51b. If $\overrightarrow{AD}$ is between $\overrightarrow{AB}$ and $\overrightarrow{AC}$, and if $\overrightarrow{AC}$ is between $\overrightarrow{AD}$ and $\overrightarrow{AE}$, (E on the D side of AB), then $\overrightarrow{AC}$ is between $\overrightarrow{AB}$ and $\overrightarrow{AE}$.

Proof: Left as an exercise.

Theorem 52. If $\overrightarrow{OB}$ is between $\overrightarrow{OA}$ and $\overrightarrow{OC}$, and if $\overrightarrow{OD}$ is the opposite ray to $\overrightarrow{OA}$, then $\overrightarrow{OC}$ is between $\overrightarrow{OB}$ and $\overrightarrow{OD}$.

Proof: Left as an exercise.

EXERCISES 5.7

1–12. Prove Theorems 41–52. (*Theorem 48)
*13. In $\angle BAC$ with $A*D*B$ and $A*C*E$, prove that D–E and B–C intersect.
*14. Given three noncollinear points, A, B, C with points D, E, F such that $B*C*D$, $A*E*C$, and $B*E*F$. Prove that F is in the interior of $\angle ACD$.
15. If $\overrightarrow{AD}$ is between $\overrightarrow{AB}$ and $\overrightarrow{AC}$, then it is false that either $\overrightarrow{AB}$ is between $\overrightarrow{AD}$ and $\overrightarrow{AC}$ or that $\overrightarrow{AC}$ is between $\overrightarrow{AD}$ and $\overrightarrow{AB}$.
*16. If $\overrightarrow{AD}$ is between $\overrightarrow{AB}$ and $\overrightarrow{AC}$, then it, together with the interiors of $\angle BAD$ and $\angle DAC$, form a partition of $\angle BAC$.
17. If $\overrightarrow{AD}$ is between $\overrightarrow{AB}$ and $\overrightarrow{AC}$, and if $\overrightarrow{AB'}$ and $\overrightarrow{AC'}$ are the opposite rays of $\overrightarrow{AB}$ and $\overrightarrow{AC}$, respectively, then $\overrightarrow{AD'}$, the ray opposite to $\overrightarrow{AD}$, is between $\overrightarrow{AB'}$ and $\overrightarrow{AC'}$.

5.8   Convex Quadrilaterals

We cannot conclude this chapter without mentioning convex quadrilaterals and pointing out that they present still another unfortunate case of a word in mathematics having more than one use.

Intuitively, when we speak of convex quadrilaterals we mean figures such as those shown in Figure 5.31 rather than those shown in Figure 5.32.

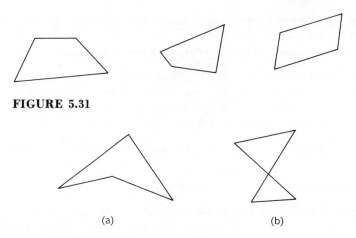

FIGURE 5.31

(a)   (b)

FIGURE 5.32

To state precisely what we mean, we shall first have to state what is meant by *quadrilateral* and then what is meant by a *convex* one.

Definition 19. Given four distinct points *A*, *B*, *C*, *D*, no three of which are collinear, the union of the four points and the four segments *A–B*, *B–C*, *C–D*, and *D–A* is called a *quadrilateral*.

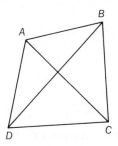

FIGURE 5.33

The points are called the *vertices;* the segments, the *sides;* the lines containing the segments, the *sidelines.*

Two sides with a common *endpoint* are called *adjacent;* two sides which are not adjacent are called *opposite.*

An *angle of a quadrilateral* is an angle which contains a vertex and two adjacent sides.

Two angles of a quadrilateral are *adjacent* if their intersection contains a side; two angles which are not adjacent are *opposite.*

The vertices of adjacent angles are called *adjacent vertices;* two vertices which are not adjacent are called *opposite vertices.*

A segment joining opposite vertices is called a *diagonal.*

As complete as this definition appears, it does not eliminate such a figure as that in Figure 5.32(b). (The reader should check for himself to find the opposite sides and the diagonals.) Because we do not want to consider such quadrilaterals, we introduce the following definition:

Definition 20. If no two sides of a quadrilateral meet it is called *simple.*

In order to exclude figures such as that in Figure 5.32(a) from this discussion, we introduce another definition:

Definition 21. If for any two adjacent vertices of a quadrilateral the vertices not on that sideline are on the same side of the sideline, then the quadrilateral is called a *convex* quadrilateral.

It is now possible to state what we mean by the interior of a quadrilateral, as long as the quadrilateral is convex.

Definition 22. The *interior* of a convex quadrilateral is the intersection of all those half planes which are determined by the sidelines and which contain the vertices not on the sidelines.

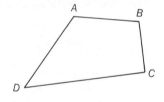

FIGURE 5.34

Thus, if $ABCD$ is a convex quadrilateral, the interior is the intersection of: (see Figure 5.34)

1. the half plane determined by AD and containing C, B.
2. the half plane determined by AB and containing D, C.
3. the half plane determined by BC and containing D, A.
4. the half plane determined by DC and containing A, B.

The definitions given would require considerable change if they were to encompass a larger range of figures. Definition 22 is worthless even for figures such as those in Figure 5.32. While we may intuitively recognize what it is we want to designate as the interior of such a figure, to define it precisely is not easy. The problem becomes even more difficult when we consider the entire range of figures called polygons. For if we were to think of a polygon as the union of segments determined by a finite number of points, together with those points, we would still have to eliminate

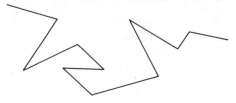

FIGURE 5.35

Figure 5.35 as an instance of a polygon. We want a polygon to enclose a region. Suppose, however, that the polygon looked like the one in Figure 5.36. It is not easy to see if it encloses a region or not, and, if so, which the

FIGURE 5.36

interior points are and which the exterior or whether the figure crosses itself or not. For the definitions given to include such complicated cases, they would need major changes.

Because we shall not need to consider anything other than quadrilaterals and triangles we have chosen the more expedient way. The reader might find it interesting to generalize these definitions for himself. He should also note the slight discrepancy in terminology. It would be consistent to speak either of a trilateral and a quadrilateral or a triangle and a quadrangle (or, perhaps, a trigon and a quadrigon). However, the other usage is well established.

It is easy to see that no triangle or quadrilateral is a convex set; but there is a relationship between the two uses of *convex* as shown by a previous theorem on triangles and the following theorem.

Theorem 53. The interior of a convex quadrilateral is a convex set.

Proof: Left as an exercise.

This theorem is false if the quadrilateral is not convex; so is the next one.

Theorem 54. The diagonals of a convex quadrilateral intersect each other.

Proof: Left as an exercise.

More theorems on convex quadrilaterals will be given in Chapter 10, where all of them will be needed.

EXERCISES 5.8

1. Prove Theorem 51.
2. Prove Theorem 52.
3. Prove Theorem 53.
4. Prove Theorem 54.
5. Prove that a simple quadrilateral is convex if and only if its diagonals intersect.
6. Prove that if a line meets one side of a quadrilateral and does not pass through a vertex, it must meet a second side.
7. Prove that if a line meets three sides of a quadrilateral it must meet the fourth.
8. Prove that a quadrilateral is *not* convex if and only if there exists a line meeting all four sides.

ADDITIONAL EXERCISES

*1. Prove that a triangle "divides" the set of all points into two non-empty subsets (interior and exterior), which together with the triangle form a partition of the set of all points.
*2. Prove a statement similar to exercise 1 for angles.
*3. Prove a statement similar to exercise 1 for convex quadrilaterals.

6 Congruence and Comparison

Intuition tells us that it would be simple to compare sizes of segments, angles, and triangles by picking them up and putting one on top of the other. If they cover one another exactly, they are of the same size; if not, it is easy to see which is the larger and which is the smaller. This method merits no consideration unless one confuses an axiomatic system with a model of the system in which segments, angles, and triangles can be picked up. And even then another problem arises.

As stated in Chapter 4, the method of moving figures to see whether or not they coincide is called *superposition*. It was indicated that even Euclid regarded the technique as crude and seldom used it. Unfortunately, he did use it to prove the *SAS* theorem at the beginning of his work and this was sufficient to make it a common tool in textbooks ever after. Of course, Euclid introduced it as a tacit assumption, whereas so-called "modern" textbooks state it as an explicit assumption, an axiom. And to make the axiom practical, these textbooks might introduce a second axiom to the effect that when an object is moved from one place to another it remains the same size. But what is meant by "remains the same size" is never discussed.

Even assuming that these two axioms are meaningful assumptions for Euclidean geometry, a question arises. If two axioms must be assumed for the sole purpose of proving the *SAS* theorem, why not merely make that theorem an axiom? In a slightly weaker form, this is just what will be done in this chapter; but this does not solve the problem of comparing segments and angles. Here, too, Euclid avoided new axioms by means of many hidden assumptions about inequalities. The purpose of this chapter is to solve these problems.

6.1   Axioms of Congruence for Segments

Language Rule 12: CONGRUENCE *is an undefined technical relation. A figure is said to be* CONGRUENT *to another.*

Notation Rule 11: When one wishes to indicate that two figures are congruent, this may be done by writing one figure on each side of the symbol

$$\cong$$

Thus, "A–B is congruent to C–D" will be denoted by:

$$A-B \cong C-D$$

Because this new relation is undefined, we must introduce some axioms to characterize it. The first of these is called a construction axiom because it allows us to say "let there be a segment $C-D$ congruent to any given segment $A-B$."

Axiom 11. The *segment construction axiom*. Given a segment $A-B$ and a point C on a line m, then on each ray on m with terminal point C there exists exactly one point D such that $A-B \cong C-D$.

The axiom does not actually tell us how to construct congruent segments; it merely tells us of their existence. It is not uncommon for a mathematician to go to great trouble to show the existence of something and then ignore the process of finding or constructing it. In our case (it will probably surprise those readers who can recall high school geometry) there will be no *need* for constructions. This is understandable if we remember that constructions are really not part of the system but of some model of the system.

There are three fundamental properties that the relation of congruence must have if it is to serve the purpose for which it was introduced. Rather than state three separate axioms, the three properties can be stated succinctly in one axiom after introducing the following rule:

Language Rule 13: Any relation R, over a set S, which satisfies the *following three properties, is called an* EQUIVALENCE RELATION *over a set S. Given that a, b, c are any elements of S,*
  (a) *aRa for every a (Read: a is related to a)*;
  (b) *if aRb, then bRa*;
  (c) *if aRb, and bRc, then aRc.*
These three conditions are called respectively; reflexive, symmetric, and transitive *properties of an equivalence relation.*

This has been stated as a language rule rather than as a definition because it has a universal scope and does not belong to the subject matter of geometry alone. With this rule it is now possible to introduce the following compact axiom:

Axiom 12. For segments, congruence is an equivalence relation.

It follows that this axiom says that every segment is congruent to itself; that, if one segment is congruent to a second, the second is congruent to the first; and that, if one segment is congruent to a second, and the second to a third, then the first is congruent to the third. Because "congruence" is an undefined relation, the only way in which these properties can be attributed to it is if they are assumed as axioms or proved as theorems. This may seem like belaboring the obvious, but think of what would have happened if instead of introducing this new relation we had used the old familiar "equals." This relation is so familiar that to have stated that it had the three properties might have indeed seemed like belaboring the obvious; it would have seemed like a definition of "equals."

But one should not now jump to the conclusion that the only thing these two relations have in common is that they are each equivalent relations. "Congruence" must have other properties in common with "equals." One of these properties is that equals added to equals are equal. This was one of Euclid's Common Notions and elementary geometry would not be the same without it; however, one should recall that Euclid, in introducing these terms, never said exactly what he meant by "addition." Such a property introduced at this time must, of necessity, be carefully restricted. Thus it will be noted that the following axiom concerns "addition" of collinear adjacent segments.

Axiom 13. (*Segment Addition*) If (a) $A*B*C$, (b) $D*E*F$, (c) $A\text{–}B \cong D\text{–}E$, and (d) $B\text{–}C \cong E\text{–}F$, then $A\text{–}C \cong D\text{–}F$.

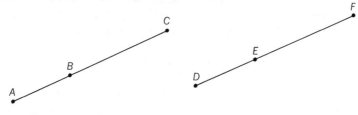

FIGURE 6.1

The following theorem says very much the same for congruent segments "subtracted" from congruent segments, given that the segments that are subtracted are subsets of the others.

Theorem 55. (*Segment Subtraction*) If (a) $A*B*C$, (b) $D*E*F$, (c) $A-B \cong D-E$, and (d) $A-C \cong D-F$, then $B-C \cong E-F$.

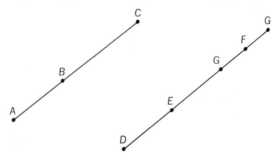

FIGURE 6.2

Proof: Suppose that the hypothesis is satisfied and the conclusion is not. Then there exists a segment $E-G$ such that $B-C \cong E-G$; that this is so follows from Axiom 11. Furthermore, since we are assuming that $E-F$ is not congruent to $E-G$, it follows from Axiom 12 that $F \neq G$. But by Axiom 13 it follows that since $A-B \cong D-E$, and $B-C \cong E-G$, $A-C \cong D-G$. However, it is given that $A-C \cong D-F$; thus from Axiom 12 it follows that $D-F \cong D-G$, and from Axioms 11 and 12 it follows that $F = G$. Hence we are led to a contradiction from the assumption that our conclusion is false; so we must conclude that $B-C \cong E-F$. •

Theorem 56. If $A-C \cong D-F$, and B is a point such that $A*B*C$, then there exists a point E such that $A-B \cong D-E$, and $D*E*F$.

Proof: Left as an exercise.

One problem the reader may find in proving Theorem 56 is that it is so obvious he keeps assuming it is true in trying to prove it. The difficult part of the theorem, of course, is to show that $D*E*F$. We leave the reader with this task and the assurance that it can be done at this time. It is a useful theorem.

EXERCISES 6.1

1. Which of the following relations are equivalence relations:

    (a) parallel   (b) perpendicular

    (c) similar to   (d) next to

    (e) isomorphic   (f) in the same class with

    (g) less than or equal to.

2. Suppose that the three properties stated in Language Rule 13 are given as axioms. Find models showing that each of the statements is independent of the others.

3. Prove Theorem 56.

6.2 Comparison of Segments

In this kind of development of geometry, in which measurement and its underlying number system are not introduced, some problems become unusually cumbersome. In the last section a means of discussing addition and subtraction of specially related segments was introduced. A discussion of addition and subtraction of segments in general, however, must be postponed until Chapter 8, where we can devote an entire chapter to this difficult problem.

On first thought it might seem equally difficult to *compare* segments, to decide which of two segments is the smaller given that they are not congruent. Strangely, this concept is no trouble whatsoever, and may be discussed fully by employing the concepts of "congruent" and "between."

Definition 23. $A–B$ is *less than* $C–D$ iff there exists a point E such that $C*E*D$, and such that $A–B \cong C–E$.

The reader should satisfy himself that this definition expresses what one usually means by *less than*.

Notation Rule 12. *"A–B is less than C–D" will be denoted by:*

$$A–B < C–D$$

We can now prove some of the standard theorems about the "less than" relation. We shall start with what is usually called the Trichotomy Law.

Theorem 57. (**Trichotomy**) If $A–B$ and $C–D$ are any two segments, then exactly one of the following conditions holds:

$$A–B < C–D, \qquad A–B \cong C–D, \qquad C–D < A–B$$

Proof: Given segments $A–B$, $C–D$, then by Axiom 11 there exists a point F on the D side of C such that $A–B \cong C–F$. Either F and D are distinct or not. If F and D are distinct, it follows from Axiom 7 that exactly one of the following conditions holds: $C*F*D$, or $C*D*F$. Hence, it follows that

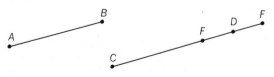

FIGURE 6.3

exactly one of the conditions, C^*F^*D, C^*D^*F, $D = F$, holds. From this, the theorem will be shown to follow.

(a) If C^*F^*D, then by Definition 23 $A-B < C-D$. Conversely, if $A-B < C-D$, then there exists a point F such that C^*F^*D and $A-B \cong C-F$; and by Axiom 11 there exists exactly one such point. Hence, C^*F^*D iff $A-B < C-D$.

(b) If C^*D^*F and $A-B \cong C-F$, then by Theorem 56 there exists a point D' such that $C-D \cong A-D'$ and $A^*D'^*B$. But then by Definition 23, $C-D < A-B$. Conversely, if $C-D < A-B$, then there exists a point E such that $C-D \cong A-E$ and A^*E^*B. By Axiom 11 there exists a point G such that C^*D^*G and $D-G \cong E-B$. Hence, by Axiom 13, $A-B \cong C-G$. But since $A-B \cong C-F$, $C-F \cong C-G$, and thus $F = G$. Therefore, by substitution, since C^*D^*G, C^*D^*F. Hence, C^*D^*F iff $C-D < A-B$.

(c) If $D = F$, then $A-B \cong C-D$. Conversely, if $A-B \cong C-D$, then by Axioms 11 and 12, $D = F$. Hence, $D = F$ iff $A-B \cong C-D$.

The equivalence of the conditions has thus been shown. Since exactly one of the conditions C^*D^*F, $D = F$, C^*F^*D, holds, exactly one of the equivalent conditions holds. •

In this chapter we have given names to some of the axioms and theorems. Although we have attempted to make these names descriptive, they should be regarded merely as memory aids to help us to refer to these axioms and theorems later in the book; otherwise, the reader would have to keep checking back to the numbers.

Not all theorems and axioms will be given names but wherever such statements illustrate specific concepts, and are important enough to be referred to frequently, some name will be attached to them. The following theorems are good examples:

Theorem 58. (*Presubstitution*) If $A-B < C-D$ and $A-B \cong E-F$, then $E-F < C-D$.

Proof: Since $A-B < C-D$, there exists a point G such that C^*G^*D and $A-B \cong C-G$; but then since it is given that $A-B \cong E-F$, it follows by transitivity that $E-F \cong C-G$. So, by Definition 23, $E-F < C-D$. •

Theorem 59. (*Postsubstitution*) If $A-B < C-D$ and $C-D \cong E-F$, then $A-B < E-F$.

Proof: By Definition 23, there exists a point G such that C^*G^*D, and $A-B \cong C-G$. By Theorem 56 there exists a point H such that E^*H^*F, and $E-H \cong C-G$. Since $A-B \cong C-G$, it follows that $A-B \cong E-H$ and, hence, that $A-B < E-F$. •

Theorem 60. (*Transitivity*) If A–B < C–D and C–D < E–F, then A–B < E–F.

Proof: Since A–B < C–D, there exists a point G such that $C*G*D$ and A–B ≅ C–G. Since C–D < E–F, there exists a point H such that $E*H*F$ and C–D ≅ E–H. It follows now from Theorem 59 that A–B < E–H and, hence, there exists a point I such that $E*I*H$ and A–B ≅ E–I. Now since $E*H*F$ and $E*I*H$, it follows from Theorem 7 that $E*I*H*F$. Hence, $E*I*F$ and we may conclude that A–B < E–F.   ●

6.3   Congruences for Angles and Triangles

In the first two sections of this chapter two new relations were introduced, namely, "congruence" and "less than." The sections were then devoted to relating *segments* by each of these relations. An exactly analogous pattern cannot be followed for *angles;* the reason for this will be given in the next section. Nevertheless, we can begin in much the same way.

Axiom 14. The *angle construction axiom.* Given an angle BAC and given a ray DF on a line m, then on each side of m there exists exactly one ray DE such that $\angle BAC \cong \angle EDF$.

Axiom 15. For angles, congruence is an equivalence relation.

We have said that to avoid the problem of superposition we will introduce a new axiom and that the axiom is almost, but not quite, Euclid's fourth theorem. This is a good time to introduce the axiom, as it not only avoids the superposition problem but serves to connect the congruence relation for segments and angles.

Axiom 16. If in triangles ABC and DEF, A–B ≅ D–E, A–C ≅ D–F, and $\angle A \cong \angle D$, then $\angle B \cong \angle E$, and $\angle C \cong \angle F$.

This axiom says that when two sides and the included angle of one triangle are congruent respectively to two sides and the included angle of another, then the remaining *angles* are congruent. How does this differ from the fourth theorem of Euclid, the *SAS* theorem? The theorem says that under the same hypothesis the two *triangles* are congruent. What else must be known to conclude that the two triangles are congruent? Before this can be answered, we need to define what it means to say that two triangles are congruent.

Given two triangles, there are six distinct ways to set up a one-one correspondence between their vertices. For example, given triangles ABC, and DEF, we can correspond their vertices as follows:

1. $A \leftrightarrow D$ $B \leftrightarrow E$ $C \leftrightarrow F$
2. $A \leftrightarrow D$ $B \leftrightarrow F$ $C \leftrightarrow E$
3. $A \leftrightarrow E$ $B \leftrightarrow D$ $C \leftrightarrow F$
4. $A \leftrightarrow E$ $B \leftrightarrow F$ $C \leftrightarrow D$
5. $A \leftrightarrow F$ $B \leftrightarrow D$ $C \leftrightarrow E$
6. $A \leftrightarrow F$ $B \leftrightarrow E$ $C \leftrightarrow D$

Furthermore, because the vertices of a triangle determine the sides, any correspondence between the vertices of two triangles sets up a correspondence between the sides; and, because angles have a unique vertex, any correspondence between vertices sets up a correspondence between angles. This is stated succinctly in the following notation.

Notation Rule 13: *By* ABC $\leftrightarrow$ DEF, *we shall mean:*

$$A \leftrightarrow D \qquad \angle A \leftrightarrow \angle D \qquad A\text{-}B \leftrightarrow D\text{-}E$$
$$B \leftrightarrow E \qquad \angle B \leftrightarrow \angle E \qquad B\text{-}C \leftrightarrow E\text{-}F$$
$$C \leftrightarrow F \qquad \angle C \leftrightarrow \angle F \qquad A\text{-}C \leftrightarrow D\text{-}F$$

Language Rule 14: *When a particular correspondence is given, the angles that correspond will be referred to as* CORRESPONDING ANGLES; *the sides that correspond will be referred to as* CORRESPONDING SIDES.

It should be apparent that any two triangles can have their vertices put into some one-one correspondence. This does not mean that any two triangles are congruent; and, even for two congruent triangles, any random pairing of vertices does not necessarily display a congruence relation. Let us express this formally.

Definition 24. Given any two triangles ABC, DEF, if there exists at least one correspondence $ABC \leftrightarrow XYZ$, where X, Y, Z are D, E, F in some order, such that

$$\angle A \cong \angle X \qquad A\text{-}B \cong X\text{-}Y$$
$$\angle B \cong \angle Y \qquad B\text{-}C \cong Y\text{-}Z$$
$$\angle C \cong \angle Z \qquad A\text{-}C \cong X\text{-}Z$$

then this correspondence is called a *congruent correspondence*. And the two triangles are said to be *congruent*.

Notation Rule 14. *If* ABC $\leftrightarrow$ DEF *is a congruent correspondence for the triangles ABC and DEF, this will be denoted by:*

$$\triangle ABC \cong \triangle DEF$$

and read "is congruent to."

It is unfortunate that once again a word is being used in two ways. We introduced "congruence" as an undefined relation that applies to segments and angles. Now we *define* what it is to say that two triangles are congruent. Fortunately, it is unlikely that this discrepancy will cause confusion.

We are finally in a position to prove the famous—or infamous—fourth theorem of Euclid, the *SAS* theorem of elementary geometry.

Theorem 61. (*SAS*) If, in one triangle, two sides and the angle containing them are respectively congruent to two sides and the angle containing them in a second triangle, then the two triangles are congruent.

Restatement. *If in triangles ABC and DEF, A–B* ≅ *D–E, A–C* ≅ *D–F and* ∠*A* ≅ ∠*D, then* △*ABC* ≅ △*DEF.*
Proof: It follows at once from Axiom 16 that ∠*B* ≅ ∠*E* and ∠*C* ≅ ∠*F*. Thus, by Definition 24, it follows that all that needs to be proved is that *B–C* ≅ *E–F*.

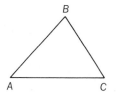 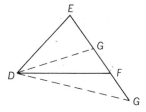

FIGURE 6.4

On the ray with terminal point *E* containing the segment *E–F*, there exists a point *G* such that *B–C* ≅ *E–G*. That this is so follows from Axiom 11. And it also follows (from what?) that if *B–C* and *E–F* are not congruent, then *G* and *F* are distinct; then, from Axiom 7, it is the case that either *E*G*F* or *E*F*G*.

Suppose that *B–C* is not congruent to *E–F*. Applying Axiom 16 to triangles *ABC* and *DEG* it follows that ∠*BAC* ≅ ∠*EDG*. However, it was given that ∠*BAC* ≅ ∠*EDF*; therefore, from Axiom 15, it may be concluded that ∠*EDF* ≅ ∠*EDG*. But this contradicts Axiom 14. (Why?)

Hence, the assumption that the segments *B–C* and *E–F* are not congruent leads to a contradiction, and is therefore false. Thus, by the Trichotomy theorem *B–C* ≅ *E–F*, and △*ABC* ≅ △*DEF*. ●

Many of the familiar theorems of elementary geometry follow from the *SAS* theorem. Those theorems needed immediately will be proved in this section; many others will be found in Chapter 7.

Some of the proofs that follow may seem rather devious. For example, the proof of Theorem 62 is as simple as cán be providing one has straight angles and a subtraction axiom for angles. In Chapter 5 it was explained why straight angles were omitted; in the next section a subtraction theorem for angles will be proved using the theorems that are now going to be proved without it. Therefore, if the proofs are devious, there is a reason for it.

Definition 25. Two angles having a common side and having the other two sides form opposite rays are said to form a *linear pair*.

Definition 26. Two angles that are respectively congruent to the angles of a linear pair are said to be *supplementary*. One is said to be the *supplement* of the other.

Theorem 62. If two angles are congruent, so also are their respective angles which form linear pairs.

Proof: Let $\angle ABC \cong \angle DEF$; let G be a point such that $A*B*G$ and let H be a point such that $D*E*H$. Then rays BA and BG are opposite rays,

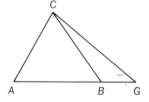 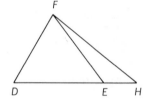

FIGURE 6.5

as are rays ED and EH; and angles ABC and CBG form a linear pair, as do angles DEF and FEH. It is no loss of generality if we choose D, H, and F in such a manner that $D-E \cong A-B$, $E-F \cong B-C$, and $E-H \cong B-G$. We wish to prove that $\angle CBG \cong \angle FEH$.

In the two triangles ABC and DEF, $A-B \cong D-E$, $\angle ABC \cong \angle DEF$, and $B-C \cong E-F$; hence, by the SAS theorem, $A-C \cong D-F$, and $\angle BAC \cong \angle EDF$. Since by Axiom 13 $A-G \cong D-H$, once again by Theorem 61 (why?) $\triangle CAG \cong \triangle FDH$. By definition it follows that $F-H \cong C-G$ and that $\angle AGC \cong \angle DHF$.

Hence, in triangles CBG and FEH $\angle BGC \cong \angle EHF$, $B-G \cong E-H$, and $G-C \cong H-F$, so by Axiom 16 it follows that $\angle CBG \cong \angle FEH$. ●

Corollary 1: *Supplements of congruent angles are congruent.*
Proof: This follows from Definition 26, Axiom 15, and Theorem 62. ●

Definition 27. Two angles with a common vertex form *vertical angles* iff the rays of one are the opposite rays of the other.

Corollary 2: *Vertical angles are congruent.*
Proof: This follows from the reflexive property of Axiom 15, Definition 27, and Theorem 62. ●

Definition 28. Two angles having a common vertex and a common ray, and having the other two rays on opposite sides of the sideline of the common ray, are called *adjacent angles.*

This definition is general enough to encompass both situations illustrated in Figure 6.6.

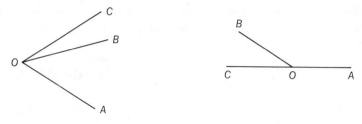

FIGURE 6.6

Corollary 3: *If two angles are supplementary and adjacent, they form a linear pair.*

Restatement: *Given* $\angle AOB$, $\angle AOC$ *supplementary where* B *and* C *are on opposite sides of line* OA. *Then rays* OB *and* OC *are opposite rays, and* $\angle AOB$, $\angle AOC$ *form a linear pair.*
Proof: Let $\overrightarrow{OD}$ be opposite to $\overrightarrow{OB}$. Then D and C are on the same side of line OA by Theorem 32. Since it is given that $\angle AOC$ and $\angle AOB$ are

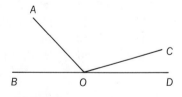

FIGURE 6.7

supplementary, and since $\angle AOD$ is the supplement of $\angle AOB$ (why?), it follows from Axiom 15 and Corollary 1 that $\angle AOC \cong \angle AOD$. Hence, by Axiom 14, rays OC and OD are the same and hence ray OC is opposite to ray OB, from which the conclusion follows. ●

EXERCISES 6.3

1. Two angles having a common vertex and a common side which lies between the other two sides are called *adjacent*. In this text, what is wrong with this "definition"?

2. Given that B–$C \cong D$–F, D–$E \cong A$–C, and $\angle C \cong \angle D$, what is the congruent correspondence for triangles ABC, DEF?

3. Supply the answer to each "why?" in the proofs of this section.

6.4   Angle Addition and Subtraction

When we discussed segments, an axiom was introduced to allow for "addition" of collinear adjacent segments; a theorem was then proved for "subtraction." In the case of angles, it is not necessary to introduce new axioms; both "addition" and "subtraction" theorems may be proved. But to do this, a bit more machinery is needed to carry the additional load. This material, which was introduced in 6.3, would have been needed even if we had chosen to introduce a new axiom for angles; introducing it at that time has thus served two purposes.

We are now in a position to prove the following theorems, analogous to Theorem 56, Axiom 13, and Theorem 55 respectively.

Theorem 63. If $\angle ABC \cong \angle DEF$ and if $\overrightarrow{BG}$ is a ray interior to $\angle ABC$ with vertex B as an endpoint, then there exists a ray EH with vertex E as endpoint and interior to $\angle DEF$, such that $\angle ABG \cong \angle DEH$, and $\angle GBC \cong \angle HEF$.

Proof: It is no loss in generality to choose D, F, so that A–$B \cong D$–E, and C–$B \cong F$–E. Then, by the SAS theorem, $\triangle ABC \cong \triangle DEF$, and A–$C \cong D$–F, $\angle BCA \cong \angle EFD$, and $\angle BAC \cong \angle EDF$.

Because A and C are arbitrary points, Theorem 50 and Definition 18 may be used to say that there exists a point M on ray BG such that $A*M*C$. Then, since A–$C \cong D$–F, and $A*M*C$, it follows from Theorem

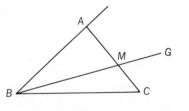
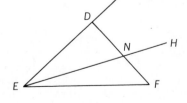

FIGURE 6.8

56 that there exists a point N such that $D-N \cong A-M$, and $D*N*F$. Thus, $\overrightarrow{EN} = \overrightarrow{EH}$ is the ray sought.

For it follows from Theorem 50 and Definition 18 that $\overrightarrow{EH}$ is interior to $\angle DEF$. From $A-C \cong D-F$, and $A-M \cong D-N$, it follows, from Theorem 55, that $M-C \cong N-F$. Therefore, it now follows (from what?) that:

$$\angle CBM = \angle CBG \cong \angle FEN = \angle FEH, \text{ hence } \angle GBC \cong \angle HEF.$$
$$\angle ABM = \angle ABG \cong \angle DEN = \angle DEH, \text{ hence } \angle ABG \cong \angle DEH. \quad \bullet$$

Theorem 64. (*Angle Addition*) Let $\angle ABC$, $\angle DEF$ be two angles that have, respectively, rays BG and EH interior with B and E as endpoints, and

$$\angle CBG \cong \angle FEH, \text{ and } \angle GBA \cong \angle HED,$$

then

$$\angle CBA \cong \angle FED.$$

Proof: By axiom 14 there exists a point M on the A side of line BC such that $\angle CBM \cong \angle FED$. By Theorem 63 there exists a point N interior to $\angle CBM$ such that $\angle CBN \cong \angle FEH$, and $\angle NBM \cong \angle HED$. But, by

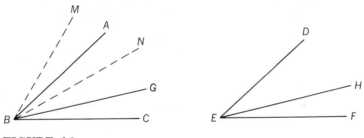

FIGURE 6.9

hypothesis, $\angle CBG \cong \angle FEH$; therefore, by Axiom 15, $\angle CBG \cong \angle CBN$ and, by Axiom 14, rays BN and BG are the same. Hence, $\angle MBN = \angle MBG \cong \angle DEH \cong \angle ABG$. Thus, $\angle MBG = \angle ABG$ and rays BM and BA are the same. So $\angle CBM = \angle CBA$ and, finally, $\angle CBA \cong \angle FED. \quad \bullet$

Theorem 65. (*Angle Subtraction*) If $\angle CBD \cong \angle GFH$ and $\angle DBA \cong \angle HFE$ and rays BA and FE are interior respectively to $\angle CBD$ and $\angle GFH$, then $\angle ABC \cong \angle EFG$. (See Figure 6.10.)

Proof: Since $\angle CBD \cong \angle GFH$ and $\overrightarrow{BA}$ is a ray interior to $\angle DBC$, it follows from Theorem 63 that there exists a point I such that $\angle DBA \cong \angle HFI$ and $\angle ABC \cong \angle IFG$. But $\angle DBA \cong \angle HFE$; hence, by Axiom 15, $\angle HFE \cong \angle HFI$ and by Axiom 14 rays FE and FI are the same. Therefore, $\angle ABC \cong \angle EFG. \quad \bullet$

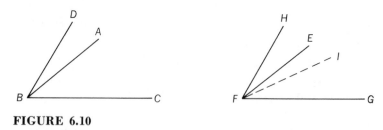

FIGURE 6.10

EXERCISES 6.4

1. Justify the last part of Theorem 63.
2. Use Theorem 39 (correctly) instead of Theorem 50 and Definition 18 to get the point M in the proof of Theorem 63.

6.5   Comparison of Angles

Definition 29. An angle $\angle ABC$ is said to be *less than* an angle $\angle DEF$ iff there exists a ray EG between rays ED and EF such that $\angle ABC \cong \angle GEF$.

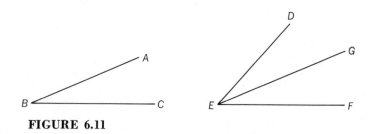

FIGURE 6.11

Notation Rule 15: *That one angle is less than another, say $\angle ABC$ less than $\angle DEF$, will be denoted by:*

$$\angle ABC < \angle DEF$$

Theorem 66. (Trichotomy) For any pair of angles, say $\angle A$ and $\angle B$, exactly one of the following conditions holds:

$$\angle A < \angle B, \qquad \angle A \cong \angle B, \qquad \angle B < \angle A$$

Proof: Left as an exercise.

Theorem 67. (Presubstitution) If $\angle A < \angle B$ and $\angle A \cong \angle C$, then $\angle C < \angle B$.

Proof: Left as an exercise.

Theorem 68. (***Postsubstitution***) If $\angle A < \angle B$ and $\angle B \cong \angle C$, then $\angle A < \angle C$.

Proof: Left as an exercise.

Theorem 69. (***Transitivity***) If $\angle A < \angle B$ and $\angle B < \angle C$, then $\angle A < \angle C$.

Proof: Left as an exercise.

EXERCISES 6.5

*1. Prove Theorem 66.
2. Prove Theorem 67.
3. Prove Theorem 68.
4. Prove Theorem 69.

7 Elementary Geometry

The concepts introduced in the last two chapters are rich in implications. Yet, despite their variety, they barely touch on the basic material presented in the usual high school geometry course. Is there a reason why more of the standard topics of elementary geometry have not been presented? It is certainly not because of disdain for such topics; nor was it an oversight. The fact is that many of the standard properties of elementary geometry are very difficult to derive, and many cannot be proved before we have arrived at this stage of development. How, then, is it done in high school?

An obvious explanation is that at the highschool level the subject matter is presented in a more intuitive, less rigorous manner. Therefore, one slides over or ignores the subtleties of the foundations. Furthermore, many common theorems are taken as axioms. Thus, it is not at all uncommon to find the SAS, ASA, and SAA theorems taken as axioms in many texts; and it is quite common to find some very elementary theorems being proved by using the parallel postulate, continuity, and similarity theory. But this is something like calling in the local police, the state police, and the FBI to help you find your morning slippers.

The purpose of this chapter is twofold: to introduce some of the important elementary theorems, and to make the order in which they are introduced as instructive as possible. The particular order in which theorems are proved may have no intrinsic value; but, from the perspective of one who is studying axiomatic systems, there is much to be learned from comparing the ways in which theorems may be ordered.

7.1 Euclid's Theorems Reproved

In the fifth century A.D., Proclus listed many alternative ways to prove some of the theorems of the *Elements*. He cites the simple proofs of the fifth theorem (that the base angles of an isosceles triangle are congruent), and the eighth theorem (the *SSS* theorem), which are now found in most textbooks on geometry, and which in this text are left as suggested exercises. These proofs are not merely simple; they also circumvent the problems inherent in Euclid's ordering.

We shall now prove the fifth, sixth, seventh, and eighth theorems of the *Elements*, in that order and in a form that adheres as closely as possible to Euclid's. Since the time of Proclus it is not likely that such an order of presentation has occurred in any text other than the *Elements* itself. Our reason for introducing it here is to show and to emphasize how Euclid relied upon diagrams in order to prove these theorems so early in his work. It will be seen that, in order to prove them without resorting to diagrams as a part of the argument, it will be necessary to use almost all of the material previously developed.

Definition 30. A triangle with two congruent sides is called an *isosceles* triangle. The angles opposite to the congruent sides are called the *base angles;* the side common to the base angles is called the *base.*

Theorem 70. In an isosceles triangle the base angles are congruent; and, if the congruent sides are produced on the opposite side of the base, the angles so formed are congruent.

Restatement: *Given a triangle ABC with A–B ≅ A–C. If F, G are points such that A*B*F and A*C*G, prove that (a) ∠CBF ≅ ∠BCG and (b) ∠ABC ≅ ∠ACB.*

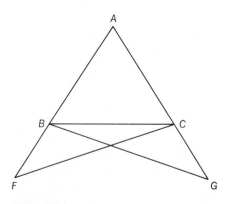

FIGURE 7.1

Proof:
Part a. Let G be a point such that $A*C*G$. By Axiom 11 there exists a point F on the B side of point A such that $A–G ≅ A–F$ and, by Axiom 11

and Theorem 56, it follows that $A*B*F$. Consider triangles ABG and ACF. Since $A-B \cong A-C$, $A-G \cong A-F$ and $\angle A \cong \angle A$, it follows from SAS that $\triangle ABG \cong \triangle ACF$. Hence, $\angle ABG \cong \angle ACF$, $\angle AGB \cong \angle AFC$, and $B-G \cong F-C$. By Theorem 55 (Segment Subtraction) it follows that $B-F \cong C-G$. Hence, once again by SAS, $\triangle FBC \cong \triangle GCB$. Therefore, $\angle CBF \cong \angle BCG$.

Part b. It is also the case that $\angle BCF \cong \angle CBG$. We now have $\angle ABG \cong \angle ACF$, $\angle CBG \cong \angle BCF$. Since $A*B*F$ and $A*C*G$, it follows that $\overrightarrow{BC}$ is interior to $\angle ABG$ and that $\overrightarrow{CB}$ is interior to $\angle ACF$. (Why?) Hence, from Theorem 65 (Angle Subtraction), it follows that $\angle ABC \cong \angle ACB$. ●

Part (a) of Theorem 70 is never seen in today's textbooks, but it is interesting to note that in our order of presentation it will soon be needed. As for part (b), there are so many ways to prove it that to list them all would not be possible. For example, one might bisect angle A and use the SAS theorem to prove that the resulting triangles are congruent. Unfortunately, this requires having all of the machinery needed for angle bisection, which we do not as yet have. A similar problem arises in most of the alternative proofs that might be suggested.

One proof of utmost simplicity was reputedly discovered by a computer a few years ago. The proof will never bear the computer's name, however, for it was known to Proclus, who attributes its discovery to Pappus about the third century A.D. In exercise 2 in Exercises 7.1 the reader may discover it once again.

The next theorem is a converse of Part (b) of Theorem 70. There are alternative proofs to this theorem also, but they depend upon the SAA theorem, which has not yet been proved. The proof given by Euclid is as simple as any. (See Figure 7.2.)

Theorem 71. If two angles of a triangle are congruent, so are the sides opposite.

Restatement: Let ABC be a triangle with $\angle B \cong \angle C$. Prove that $A-B \cong A-C$.

Proof: Suppose that $A-B$ and $A-C$ are not congruent. Then by Theorem 57 (Trichotomy for Segments) either $A-B < A-C$, or $A-C < A-B$. Suppose that $A-C < A-B$. Then (Definition 23) there exists a point D such that $A*D*B$ and $D-B \cong A-C$. Now in triangles DBC and ACB, $D-B \cong A-C$, $B-C \cong B-C$, and $\angle ABC = \angle DBC \cong \angle ACB$. Hence, by SAS, $\triangle DBC \cong \triangle ACB$. But then $\angle BCD \cong \angle CBD$ and since $\angle ACB \cong \angle CBD$, it follows that $\angle BCD \cong \angle ACB$. (Why?) This is impossible. (Why?) Since a similar argument holds if $A - B < A - C$, the supposition is false and the theorem is true. ●

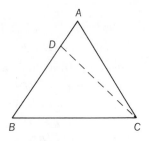

FIGURE 7.2

The next theorem can hardly be considered one of the common theorems of elementary geometry; it is seldom, if ever, mentioned in standard texts. Two good reasons for this are that its proof is very complicated and that the theorem is seldom needed. Nevertheless, its omission is unfortunate, for it says, in effect, that a triangle is a rigid figure; that is, that on one side of a line, exactly one triangle can exist having a given segment as a base and two given segments as sides. (That this property does not hold for all geometric figures is apparent to anyone who has ever tried to put up a wooden framework building; the rectangles, if left unattended, are forever shifting into parallelograms of assorted angular measures.)

Theorem 72. Given segment A–B, and given A–$C \cong A$–D, B–C $\cong B$–D, and C and D on the same side of line AB, prove that $C = D$.

Proof: Suppose not. Then $\overrightarrow{AD}$ is between $\overrightarrow{AC}$ and $\overrightarrow{AB}$, or is exterior to angle CAB, or coincides with $\overrightarrow{AC}$. And point D is interior to, exterior to, or on one of the sidelines of triangle ABC. (See last exercises, p. 104.)

Case 1. Axiom 11 rules out D coinciding with $\overrightarrow{AC}$ or $\overrightarrow{BC}$. Hence, D cannot fall on the triangle or an extension of its sides.

Case 2. If D falls exterior to triangle ABC, then since C and D are on the same side of line AB, we have either $\overrightarrow{AD}$ between $\overrightarrow{AC}$ and $\overrightarrow{AB}$, or $\overrightarrow{AC}$ between $\overrightarrow{AD}$ and $\overrightarrow{AB}$.

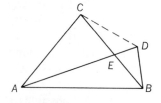

FIGURE 7.3

Subcase a. Suppose $\overrightarrow{AD}$ is between $\overrightarrow{AC}$ and $\overrightarrow{AB}$. Since $A\text{–}C \cong A\text{–}D$, by Theorem 70 $\angle ACD \cong \angle ADC$, but since D is exterior to triangle ACB, $\overrightarrow{CB}$ is between $\overrightarrow{CA}$ and $\overrightarrow{CD}$; therefore, by definition, $\angle DCB < \angle ACD$, and hence by Theorem 68 (Postsubstitution) $\angle DCB < \angle ADC$. Since $\overrightarrow{AD}$ is interior to $\angle CAB$, it crosses $B\text{–}C$ at a point E that is interior to $\angle CDB$ and hence $\overrightarrow{DA}$ is interior to $\angle CDB$, and $\angle ADC < \angle CDB$. By Theorem 69 (Transitivity) it then follows that $\angle DCB < \angle CDB$. But since $B\text{–}C \cong D\text{–}B$, $\angle CDB \cong \angle DCB$, which contradicts Theorem 66 (Trichotomy).

Subcase b. Suppose $\overrightarrow{AC}$ is between $\overrightarrow{AD}$ and $\overrightarrow{AB}$. Then either $\overrightarrow{BD}$ is between $\overrightarrow{BA}$ and $\overrightarrow{BC}$, in which case the argument proceeds as in Subcase a, or $\overrightarrow{BC}$ is between $\overrightarrow{BA}$ and $\overrightarrow{BD}$. Suppose the latter. Extend $\overrightarrow{AD}$ to F and $\overrightarrow{AC}$

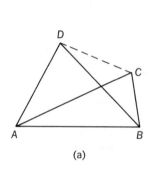
(a)

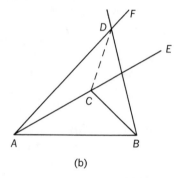
(b)

FIGURE 7.4

to E. Since $A\text{–}D \cong A\text{–}C$, triangle ACD is isosceles and $\angle FDC \cong \angle ECD$ (angles under the base are congruent). Since $\overrightarrow{AC}$ is between $\overrightarrow{AD}$ and $\overrightarrow{AB}$ and $\overrightarrow{BC}$ is between $\overrightarrow{BA}$ and $\overrightarrow{BD}$, C is a point interior to triangle ADB and hence C is interior to $\angle ADB$. (Why?) Now since $A*D*F$, F and C are on opposite sides of line BD and hence $F\text{–}C$ intersects $D\text{–}B$. (Why?) Thus $\overrightarrow{DB}$ is between $\overrightarrow{DC}$ and $\overrightarrow{DF}$ and $\angle BDC < \angle FDC$; thus from Theorem 68 (Postsubstitution) $\angle BDC < \angle ECD$. But it is easy to show that $\overrightarrow{CE}$ is interior to $\angle BCD$ and hence $\angle ECD < \angle BCD$. Thus, by Theorem 69 (Transitivity), $\angle BDC < \angle BCD$. But since $B\text{–}C \cong B\text{–}D$, $\angle BDC \cong \angle BCD$. This contradicts Theorem 66 (Trichotomy).

Case 3. If D falls interior to triangle ABC, the proof is similar to that just completed.

Because we have now eliminated all possible cases where $C \neq D$, it now follows that $C = D$ and the theorem is proved. ●

A specific reason that one seldom sees Theorem 72 is that the only use Euclid made of it was in proving his *SSS* theorem; but, from the time of Philo, who lived shortly after Euclid, an alternative proof of the *SSS* theorem has been used. This proof, which is left as exercise 7 in Exercises 7.1, does not require Theorem 72.

Once Theorem 72 has been proved, however, Euclid's proof of the *SSS* theorem is actually much simpler than the one attributed to Philo. We can present it now:

Theorem 73. (*SSS*) If three sides of a triangle are respectively congruent to three sides of another, the two triangles are congruent.

Proof: If in two triangles *ABC* and *DEF* the three sides of one are respectively congruent to three sides of the other, and if one pair of angles are congruent, say ∠*ABC* ≅ ∠*DEF*, then by *SAS*, △*ABC* ≅ △*DEF*. So suppose not; suppose that ∠*DEF* < ∠*ABC*.

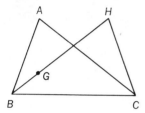 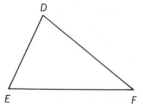

FIGURE 7.5

By Axiom 14 there exists a point *G* interior to ∠*ABC* such that ∠*GBC* = ∠*HBC* ≅ ∠*DEF*. Let *B–H* ≅ *E–D*; then since *B–C* ≅ *E–F*, △*HBC* ≅ △*DEF*. Now *H–B* ≅ *D–E* and *H–C* ≅ *D–F*; but since $\overrightarrow{BH}$ is not the same as $\overrightarrow{BA}$, this is impossible, by Theorem 72. (Why?)

Similarly, if ∠*ABC* < ∠*DEF*.

Hence, ∠*ABC* ≅ ∠*DEF* and △*ABC* ≅ △*DEF*.   ●

We are now going to have to depart from Euclid's sequence of theorems. The reason for this will be explained in the next section; but, before starting that material, it will be useful to have part of his twenty-sixth theorem, which can be proved following the *SAS* Theorem.

Theorem 74. (*ASA*) Given that two angles and the included side of one triangle are respectively congruent to two angles and the included side of another triangle, the triangles are congruent.

Restatement: *Given two triangles ABC and DEF and ∠ABC ≅ ∠DEF, and ∠ACB ≅ ∠DFE, and B–C ≅ E–F, prove that △ABC ≅ △DEF.*

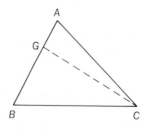 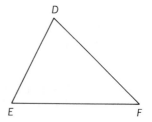

FIGURE 7.6

Proof: Suppose that $D–E < A–B$; there exists a point G such that $A*G*B$ and $B–G ≅ D–E$, and hence with $B–C ≅ E–F$, $∠GBC ≅ ∠DEF$, $△GBC ≅ △DEF$ by SAS. Hence $∠GCB ≅ ∠DFE$; but $∠DFE ≅ ∠ACB$; therefore, $∠GCB ≅ ∠ACB$. But since $A*G*B$, $∠GCB < ∠ACB$. This contradicts Theorem 66 (Trichotomy).

Similarly, if $A–B < D–E$.

Hence, $A–B ≅ D–E$ and by SAS $△ABC ≅ △DEF$.   ●

EXERCISES 7.1

1. Shorten the proof of Theorem 70 by using Theorem 62.
2. Prove Theorem 70 directly from Theorem 61 (SAS).
3. Define *equilateral* and *equiangular* as applied to triangles.
4. Prove that every equilateral triangle is equiangular.
5. Prove Theorem 71 directly from the ASA theorem.
6. Prove that every equiangular triangle is equilateral.
7. Prove the SSS theorem by the following means: given triangles ABC, DEF with three sides respectively congruent to three sides.

(a) Construct triangle $AB'C$ with B' on the opposite side of line AC from B, so that $△AB'C ≅ △DEF$.

(b) Show that $△ABC ≅ △AB'C$, and hence that $△ABC ≅ △DEF$ by considering the following three cases. Join $B–B'$ intersecting line AC at G, then
   (i) $A*G*C$.
   (ii) $A = G$.
   (iii) $G*A*C$.
   (Do we need transitivity of congruent *triangles*?)

7.2   The Exterior Angle Theorem

In the last section, for the instructive purposes suggested, we presented the theorems in the order they occur in the *Elements*. We shall now deviate from that order, as a matter of necessity rather than for any instructive purpose.

The theorems immediately following the *SSS* theorem in the *Elements*[2] have to do with constructions that show the existence of angle bisectors, midpoints of segments, and perpendicular bisectors. Unfortunately, they in turn depend either directly or indirectly on constructions that assume continuity properties of lines and circles. We must therefore find either some other manner of proving the existence of bisectors and midpoints or some other manner of proving the theorems which depend upon these properties.

A most important theorem immediately occurs. In Chapter 4 the special significance of Theorem 16 of Euclid, the "exterior angle" theorem, was mentioned. We shall soon see how useful and how powerful it is. First, however, it must be proved; and that is easier said than done.

A brief examination of Euclid's proof of this theorem reveals the first problem, for he depends on the fact that any segment has a midpoint. He has previously supplied a constructive proof of this fact, a proof which requires continuity. Therefore, our first problem seems to be to prove that any segment has a midpoint; but there are not many avenues of attack left open to us.

If one scans the literature of geometry, one is at first tempted to believe that there is no way to introduce the existence of a midpoint except by fiat (axiom) or by making some continuity assumption. Yet we can find other methods.

We might, for example, attempt to prove the existence of a unique angle bisector and use this to prove the existence of a midpoint.[3] Or we might simply try to prove the existence of a midpoint directly. Consider the following simple "proof":

Given a segment A–B, there exists a point C such that $A*B*C$ and such that A–$B \cong B$–C. Hence, B is the midpoint of segment A–C.

(Why does this proof of the existence of a midpoint fail?)

Now consider the following more sophisticated attempt. At the end-

---

[2] See Appendix, pp. 219–220.
[3] See H. G. Forder, *The Foundations of Euclidean Geometry*.

points of a line segment construct, on opposite sides of the segment, two
congruent angles; mark off congruent segments on each side of the angle
as illustrated in Figure 7.7. Then, if it can be proved that $A-E \cong E-B$, E
is the midpoint of $A-B$.

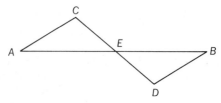

FIGURE 7.7

To prove that $A-E \cong E-B$, however, it must be shown that triangles
ACE and BDE are congruent; and to do this requires the SAA theorem.
But the SAA theorem, in turn, seems to require the exterior angle
theorem in its proof. If the exterior angle theorem then requires that any
segment must have a midpoint, we have returned full circle to the basis of
our trouble.

It becomes apparent, after working with this problem long enough,
that the exterior angle theorem is the cornerstone. On this theorem proofs
of the others may be made to rest. But for this to be so we must find some
way to prove it without resorting to the use of a midpoint. Such a proof
does exist, and it dictates the order in which the following theorems are
presented.

Theorem 75. Given a line m and a point A not on m, there exists at
least one line through A not intersecting m.

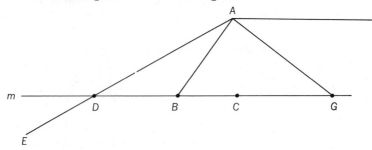

FIGURE 7.8

Proof: Take any two points B, C on m and join A and B. It follows from
the angle construction axiom that, on the side of $A-B$ opposite to C, there
exists an angle $\angle EAB$ congruent to $\angle ABC$. The line EA which so exists
does not intersect m.

For suppose it does intersect m in some point D. Then D either falls on the C side of B or does not.

Suppose not; then there exists a point G such that $D*B*G$ and such that $A–D \cong B–G$. Since $\angle BAD \cong \angle ABG$, and $B–A \cong B–A$, $\triangle ADB \cong \triangle BGA$. Therefore, $\angle ABD \cong \angle BAG$, and since $\angle ABD$ and $\angle ABG$ form a linear pair, it must be the case that $\angle BAG$, $\angle BAD$ are supplements; hence, by Corollary 3, Theorem 62, they form a linear pair. Thus D, A, G are collinear; but $A–D$, $A–G$ intersect m. This contradicts Theorem 4.

The argument is valid regardless of which side of B the point D falls on. The supposition that line EA intersects m leads to a contradiction and thus must be false. Therefore, the theorem is proved. ●

This theorem and the next one to be stated introduce issues that extend far beyond their immediate use in proving the exterior angle theorem. For one thing, the word "parallel" will not be introduced into this text formally until Chapter 9; thus, lines that we are accustomed to calling "parallel" will be called "nonintersecting."

It should also be pointed out that we have just proved that there exists *at least one* "parallel" through a given point to a given line. This should be kept in mind, because one of the main aims of this text is to show that from the axiom set that we have introduced it is impossible to prove that there exists *at most one* "parallel" through a given point to a given line.

Returning now to the main task of this section, we state some useful theorems and definitions:

Definition 31. A line intersecting two other lines in two distinct points is called a *transversal*.

Definition 32. If two lines are met in two distinct points A, B by a transversal, the angles having segment $A–B$ as a part of a side are called *interior* angles. The others are called *exterior*. Pairs of angles, one at each point A, B on the same side of the transversal, one interior, one exterior, are called *corresponding* angles. Two nonadjacent angles on opposite sides of the transversal and both interior are called *alternate interior* angles.

Theorem 76. If two lines met by a transversal have alternate interior angles congruent, the two lines are nonintersecting.

Proof: Same as the proof of the previous theorem, given Definition 32. ●

The following two theorems are included for future reference.

Theorem 77. If two lines met by a transversal have corresponding angles congruent, the lines are nonintersecting.

Proof: Left as an exercise.

Theorem 78. If two lines met by a transversal have the interior angles on the same side supplementary, the two lines are nonintersecting.

Proof: Left as an exercise.

Definition 33. An angle adjacent and supplementary to an angle of a triangle is called an *exterior angle* of the triangle. The angles of a triangle not adjacent to an exterior angle are called its *opposite interior angles*. An exterior angle of a triangle not adjacent to an angle, say $\angle A$, of the triangle is called an *opposite exterior* angle of $\angle A$.

As should be noted from the definition, the terms *opposite interior* and *opposite exterior* are terms that have meaning relative to specific angles.

Finally we come to the key theorem of this section:

Theorem 79. Any interior angle of a triangle is less than an opposite exterior angle.

Restatement: *Given a triangle ABC and a point D such that A*B*D, then $\angle CBD$ is an exterior angle of triangle ABC. Prove that $\angle BCA < \angle CBD$ and $\angle BAC < \angle CBD$.*

Proof:

Part a. By Theorem 76 it is impossible for $\angle CBD \cong \angle BCA$.

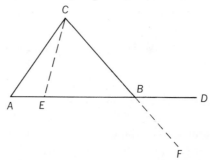

FIGURE 7.9

Part b. Suppose that $\angle CBD < \angle BCA$. Then by Definition 29 there exists a ray CE interior to $\angle ACB$ such that $\angle ECB \cong \angle CBD$. And by Theorem 48 the ray cuts $A-B$, say at a point E. But now in triangle BCE, $\angle BCE \cong \angle CBD$, which contradicts Part a. Since by Theorem 66 (Trichotomy) one of the relations holds, it must hold that $\angle BCA < \angle CBD$.

By letting F be a point such that $C*B*F$, and using Corollary 2 of Theorem 62 and $\angle ABF$, the above argument carries through to show that $\angle BAC < \angle ABF$, $\angle ABF \cong \angle CBD$, or finally $\angle BAC < \angle CBD$. ●

This proof raises an interesting theoretical question. Recall the comments made in Chapter 4 after Euclid's proof of this theorem. It was said that Euclid tacitly assumes that lines are of infinite length and that otherwise, if lines are considered to be finite in length but boundless, his proof fails. But what is to be made of this now?

The proof we have given is entirely different. If there are no assumptions hidden somewhere in the proof to which similar criticisms can be made, it has far-reaching implications. For it is amazing how many theorems are dependent on the exterior angle theorem, and whether this theorem is to hold true or not drastically alters the system. In this proof there is no apparent assumption that lines are infinite; yet this theorem is false if lines are taken to be of finite length—as, for example, on the surface of a sphere. We shall return to this problem later.

Meanwhile, we shall postpone the midpoint theorem until the next section and finish this section with several of the most useful theorems that depend on Theorem 79.

Theorem 80. (*SAA*) If two angles and a nonincluded side of one triangle are respectively congruent to two angles and a nonincluded side of the other, the two triangles are congruent.

Restatement: Given triangle ABC and triangle DEF. If $A-B \cong D-E$, $\angle B \cong \angle E$, $\angle C \cong \angle F$, prove that $\triangle ABC \cong \triangle DEF$.
Proof: If $B-C \cong E-F$, then the triangles are congruent by *ASA* or *SAS*. Suppose $B-C$ is not congruent to $E-F$. Suppose $E-F < B-C$. Then there exists a point H such that $B*H*C$ and $B-H \cong E-F$. Then $\triangle ABH \cong \triangle DEF$ by *SAS*. Hence, $\angle BHA \cong \angle EFD$; but $\angle BCA = \angle HCA \cong \angle EFD$. Therefore, in triangle AHC, exterior angle $\angle BHA \cong \angle BCA$, which contradicts Theorem 79.

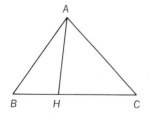 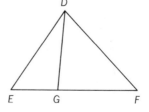

FIGURE 7.10

If $B-C < E-F$, then there exists a point G such that $E*G*F$ and $E-G \cong B-C$. The argument proceeds as above. Hence, we may conclude that $B-C \cong E-F$, and that $\triangle ABC \cong \triangle DEF$ by *SAS*. ●

Theorem 81. If two sides of a triangle are not congruent, then the angles opposite them are not congruent and the lesser angle is opposite the lesser side.

Restatement: *Given triangle ABC. If A–B < A–C, then ∠ACB < ∠ABC.*
Proof: Let *ABC* be a triangle having *A–B < A–C*. Let *D* be a point

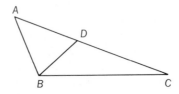

FIGURE 7.11

such that *A*D*C* and *A–D* ≅ *A–B*. Then ∠*ADB* is an *exterior* angle of triangle *BDC*, and hence ∠*DCB* < ∠*ADB* by Theorem 79. But by Theorem 70 ∠*ADB* ≅ ∠*ABD*, and hence by Theorem 68 (Postsubstitution), ∠*DCB* < ∠*ABD* or, since ∠*ACB* = ∠*DCB*, ∠*ACB* < ∠*ABD*. But *A*D*C*; hence, by definition ∠*ABD* < ∠*ABC*; therefore, by Theorem 69 (Transitivity), ∠*ACB* < ∠*ABC*. ●

Theorem 82. If two angles of a triangle are not congruent, then the sides opposite them are not congruent and the lesser side is opposite the lesser angle.

Restatement: *Given triangle ABC. If ∠BCA < ∠ABC, then A–B < A–C.*
Proof: Suppose not. Then *A–B* ≅ *A–C* or *A–C* < *A–B*.

If *A–B* ≅ *A–C*, then it follows from Theorem 70 that ∠*ABC* ≅ ∠*BCA* contrary to hypothesis. If *A–C* < *A–B*, then by Theorem 81 ∠*ABC* < ∠*BCA*, which once again is contrary to hypothesis and Theorem 66 (Trichotomy).

By Theorem 57 (Trichotomy), the other two being ruled out, *A–B* < *A–C*. ●

EXERCISES 7.2

1. By the angle construction axiom, the angle *EAB* in Theorem 75 is unique. Hence there exists a unique line *EA*. Hence there exists *at most one* line through *A* parallel to *m*. What is wrong with this "proof"?

2. Prove Theorem 77.

3. Prove Theorem 78.

7.3 Midpoints and Halves

Definition 34. If C is a point such that $A*C*B$, and A–$C \cong C$–B, then C is called a *midpoint* of segment A–B.

The following lemma will be helpful in proving the existence of a midpoint; we could, of course, incorporate them into a single theorem, but separating them will clarify what is being done.

Lemma 1: *Given any segment A–B, if $\angle ABY$ and $\angle BAX$ are on opposite sides of A–B and are such that $\angle ABY \cong \angle BAX$, then if D is any point on $\overrightarrow{BY}$ and C is any point on $\overrightarrow{AX}$, then C–D intersects line AB in a point E such that $A*E*B$.*

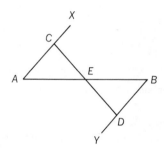

FIGURE 7.12

Proof: C–D must intersect line AB in some point E because C and D are on opposite sides of line AB. Thus $A*E*B$, or $A*B*E$, or $E*A*B$. (Why? Why not $E = A$ or $E = B$?)
  Suppose $E*A*B$.

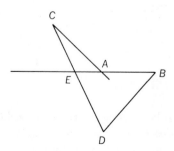

FIGURE 7.13

Then line CA meets B–E, a side of triangle EBD and, by Axiom 10, must then meet another side; but this is impossible. For line CA meets line DE at C and thus cannot do so again; and, by Theorem 76, line CA is nonintersecting with line BD.

Suppose $A*B*E$.

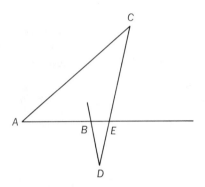

FIGURE 7.14

Then line DB meets A–E, a side of triangle AEC and, by Axiom 10, must then meet another side; but this is impossible. For line BD meets line CE at D and thus cannot do so again; and, by Theorem 76, line BD is nonintersecting with line AC.

Having eliminated the other two relations we may conclude that $A*E*B$. ●

Theorem 83. Any segment has (a) at least one midpoint, (b) at most one midpoint.

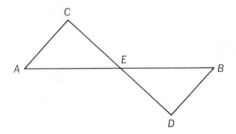

FIGURE 7.15

Proof: Part a. Let A–B be any segment, and let $\angle ABD$ and $\angle BAC$ be two angles on opposite sides of A–B such that $\angle ABD \cong \angle BAC$. Let A–C $\cong B$–D. Then by Lemma 1, C–D intersects line AB at a point E such that $A*E*B$. By assumption, $\angle CAE \cong \angle EBD$ and A–$C \cong B$–D; by Theorem

62, Corollary 2, $\angle CEA \cong \angle BED$. So by *SAA* $\triangle ACE \cong \triangle BDE$. Therefore, $A-E \cong E-B$ and E is a midpoint of $A-B$.

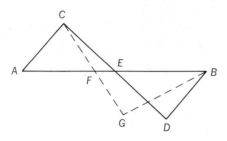

FIGURE 7.16

Part b. Suppose now that there exists a point F such that $A*F*B$ and $A-F \cong F-B$. On ray CF, take $F-G \cong C-F$. Then by *SAS* $\triangle ACF \cong \triangle BGF$, from which it follows that $\angle FBG \cong \angle FAC \cong \angle ABD$ and $B-G \cong A-C \cong B-D$. Therefore, $G = D$ and $F = E$. (Why?) ●

Definition 35. If C is a midpoint of segment $A-B$, then $A-C$ is called a *half* of $A-B$; $A-C$, $C-B$ are called *halves*.

Theorem 84. Halves of congruent segments are congruent.

Restatement: *If* $A-B \cong C-D$, *and* $A*E*B$, $C*F*D$, $A-E \cong E-B$, $C-F \cong F-D$, *then* $A-E \cong C-F$.
Proof: If $A-B \cong C-D$ and $A*E*B$, then by Theorem 56 there exists a point G such that $C*G*D$ and $A-E \cong C-G$. Then by Theorem 55 (Seg-

FIGURE 7.17

ment Subtraction), $E-B \cong G-D$. By hypothesis, $A-E \cong E-B$; therefore, by transitivity, $C-G \cong G-D$. Now we have $C*G*D$ and $C-G \cong G-D$; so, by Definition 34, G is a midpoint. By Theorem 83, Part (b), $F = G$; so, by substitution, $A-E \cong C-F$. ●

Definition 36. A ray OD is said to *bisect* an angle $\angle AOB$ iff (a) D is interior to $\angle AOB$, (b) $\angle AOD \cong \angle DOB$.

Theorem 85. Every angle has a bisector.

Proof: Left as an exercise.

Theorem 86. Every angle has at most one bisector.

Proof: Left as an exercise.

Definition 37. If $\overrightarrow{OD}$ is a bisector of $\angle AOB$, then $\angle AOD$ is called a *half* of $\angle AOB$; $\angle AOD$, $\angle BOD$ are called *halves*.

Theorem 87. Halves of congruent angles are congruent.

Proof: Left as an exercise.

EXERCISES 7.3

1. Prove Theorem 85.
2. Prove Theorem 86.
3. Prove Theorem 87.
4. Define what is meant by a *median*.
5. Prove that in an isosceles triangle the bisector of the nonbase angle is also a median.

*6. Prove that in a triangle if the bisector of an angle is also a median, the triangle is isosceles.

*7. Without using a midpoint consider $\angle BAC$ with $A*E*B$, $A*D*C$, $A\text{–}E \cong A\text{–}D$, $A\text{–}B \cong A\text{–}C$. Then using $B\text{–}D$, $C\text{–}E$ (and exercise 13, Exercises 5.7) prove the existence of a unique angle bisector.

7.4 Right Angles and Non-right Angles

In a metric approach to geometry, most of the theorems in this section would be quite trivial. In a nonmetric approach such as this, many of them are difficult to prove. We have gathered them together in this section for the sake of unity; some of them could have been proved earlier, given the needed definitions.

Definition 38. An angle congruent to its supplementary angle is called a *right* angle. An angle less than a right angle is called an *acute* angle. Any angle that is neither right nor acute is called *obtuse*.

Theorem 88. Any acute angle is less than any obtuse angle.

Proof: Left as an exercise.

Theorem 89a. An angle is obtuse iff its supplementary angle is acute.

Proof: Left as an exercise. (Suggestion: use Theorem 52.)

Theorem 89b. If two angles are supplementary and unequal, one of them is acute.

Proof: Left as an exercise.

Theorem 90. Any angle congruent to a right angle is a right angle.

Proof: Left as an exercise.

Theorem 91. If right angles exist, then at least two angles of any triangle are acute.

Proof: Left as an exercise.

The next theorem is proved by Hilbert; it is one of the few theorems actually proved in the *Foundations*. As can be seen, the proof is far from trivial; perhaps that is why Euclid chose to make it an axiom.

Theorem 92. All right angles are congruent.

Restatement: *Let ∠BAD, ∠CAD be congruent and form a linear pair; let ∠FEH, ∠GEH be congruent and form a linear pair. Prove that ∠BAD ≅ ∠FEH.*

Proof: Suppose not. Then (a) ∠FEH < ∠BAD or (b) ∠BAD < ∠FEH. Consider case (a). There exists a point J interior to ∠BAD such that

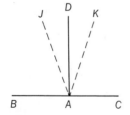 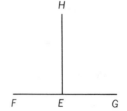

FIGURE 7.18

∠BAJ ≅ ∠FEH. Because ∠BAJ ≅ ∠FEH, then by Theorem 62' Corollary 1, ∠CAJ ≅ ∠GEH; but, by hypothesis, ∠FEH ≅ ∠GEH; so by transitivity ∠BAJ ≅ ∠CAJ.

Now since ∠BAD ≅ ∠CAD, it follows from Theorem 63 that there exists a ray AK which is interior to ∠CAD and is such that ∠BAJ ≅ ∠CAK (and ∠JAD ≅ ∠KAD). But we have shown that ∠BAJ ≅ CAJ; therefore, by transitivity, ∠CAJ ≅ ∠CAK. This is impossible. (Why?) Hence, the assumption that ∠FEH < ∠BAD leads to a contradiction and so must be false. A similar argument carries through for case (b). Therefore, by Theorem 66 (Trichotomy), the theorem is proved. ●

Neither this theorem nor any one that precedes it guarantees the existence of a single right angle. Theorem 92 is simply not an existence theorem; it merely says that *if* one or more right angles exist they are congruent. That right angles do indeed exist will be proved, in effect, by the next theorem.

Theorem 93, in itself, is not surprising. But it is somewhat surprising that such a theorem is provable in a system where continuity has not been introduced. For it says that given *any* point not on a given line there exists a perpendicular from that point to the given line; and in the proof it is shown that the point at the "foot" of the perpendicular exists. This takes us back to the "Plane Separation Theorem," whose proof is equally surprising in a system lacking continuity criteria.

The following definition and rules will be of use in stating and proving the rest of the theorems of this section.

Definition 39. Two distinct rays are called *perpendicular* iff they have common terminal points and if the angle which is their union is a right angle.

Language Rule 15: *We shall also refer to the segments or lines which colline with perpendicular rays as being perpendicular. In the case of segments, we shall usually want them to intersect or have an endpoint in common before we refer to them as perpendicular.*

Notation Rule 16: *That two rays $\overrightarrow{OA}$ and $\overrightarrow{OB}$ are perpendicular will be denoted by:*

$$\overrightarrow{OA} \perp \overrightarrow{OB}$$

This symbol will also be used as follows:

$$O\text{-}A \perp O\text{-}B \qquad OA \perp OB$$

Theorem 93. Given a line and a point *not* on the line, there exists *at least one* line perpendicular to the given line and through the point.

Proof: Given a line m, a point A not on m, and any point B on m. On the opposite side of m from A there exists a ray $\overrightarrow{BX}$ which makes with m an angle congruent to the angle which $\overrightarrow{BA}$ makes with m. There exists a point C on $\overrightarrow{BX}$ such that $B\text{-}C \cong B\text{-}A$. Then $A\text{-}C$ intersects m at a point D. (Why?) If by chance $B = D$, then line AC must be perpendicular to m. (Why?) If $B \neq D$, then $\triangle ABD \cong \triangle CBD$ by SAS. Hence, $\angle BDC \cong \angle BDA$ and they are right angles. (Why?) In either case we have shown that if A is a point not on m, there exists at least one line through A which is perpendicular to m. ● (See Figure 7.19.)

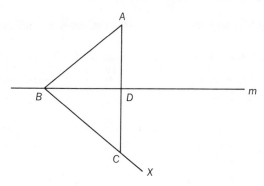

FIGURE 7.19

Theorem 94. Given a line and a point *not* on the line, there exists *at most one* line perpendicular to the given line and through the point.

Proof: Left as an exercise.

Theorem 95. Given a line and a point *on* the line, there exists *at least one* line perpendicular to the given line, and through the point.

Proof: By Theorem 93 and Definition 39 we know that right angles exist. Let A be a point on m and let C be any other point of m; then, by the

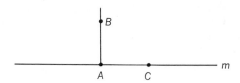

FIGURE 7.20

angle construction axiom, there exists a point B such that $\angle CAB$ is congruent to a right angle. So, by Theorem 90, $\angle CAB$ *is* a right angle. By Definition 39, the theorem follows. ●

Theorem 96. Given a line and a point *on* the line, there exists *at most one* line perpendicular to the given line and through the given point.

Proof: Left as an exercise.

Definition 40. A line through the midpoint of a segment and perpendicular to the segment is called a *perpendicular bisector* of the segment.

Theorem 97. Every segment has exactly one perpendicular bisector.

Proof: Left as an exercise.

Definition 41. A point C is said to be *equidistant* from two points A and B, iff A–$C \cong C$–B.

Theorem 98. A point is equidistant from the endpoints of a segment iff it lies on the perpendicular bisector of the segment.

Proof: Left as an exercise.

Definition 42. Given a line and any point not on the line, then any segment having as endpoints the given point and a point on the given line is called an *oblique*, iff it is distinct from the perpendicular.

Theorem 99. The perpendicular segment from a point not on a line to a point on the line is less than any oblique.

Proof: Left as an exercise.

EXERCISES 7.4

1. Prove Theorem 88.
2. Prove Theorem 89.
3. Prove Theorem 90.
4. Prove Theorem 91.
5. Prove Theorem 94.
6. Prove Theorem 96.
7. Prove Theorem 97.
8. Prove Theorem 98.
9. Prove Theorem 99.
10. Define what is meant by a *right* triangle.
11. Define what is meant by the *hypotenuse* of a right triangle.
*12. If the hypotenuse and one side of a right triangle are congruent respectively to the hypotenuse and a side of another right triangle, the two triangles are congruent. Prove this.
13. Define what is meant by the *altitude* of a triangle.
14. Prove that a triangle is isosceles if and only if:

(a) a median to one side is also an altitude.

(b) a bisector of an angle is also an altitude.

(c) a perpendicular bisector of a side is also an altitude.

(d) a perpendicular bisector of a side is also a median.

(e) a perpendicular bisector of a side is also an angle bisector.

7.5   Constructions

We have stated repeatedly that it is all right to use diagrams if they are used merely as an aid to intuition and do not become a part of the structure of a proof. But what is to become, then, of constructions? Are they not simply "controlled" diagrams?

Euclid certainly regarded constructions differently. This is attested to by his Theorems 9, 10, 11, 12, and 23, which are useful theorems in his system.[4] He not only used them to justify constructions of angle bisectors and perpendicular bisectors of segments but relied on them in place of existence theorems. In contrast, our system has introduced the angle and segment construction axioms and we have proved such theorems as 86, 93, 95, and 97; but these theorems are merely existence theorems. Consider Theorem 93. At first sight, its proof seems to present a means of actually constructing a perpendicular to a line from a point not on it; but observe that it says *let* such and such be an angle congruent to another angle. If we cannot *construct* an angle congruent to a given angle, we cannot actually construct the perpendicular by using Theorem 93.

To discuss the subject of constructions at all we shall regard them as that which occurs only in some *model* of our system.   Euclid used a straightedge and compass in his constructions; because we have not yet introduced circles, we shall omit the compass.   However, in order to make some of these elementary constructions, more than the use of a straightedge is required; therefore, we shall make the following assumptions:

1. With a straightedge, we may draw (that is, construct) a line determined by any two points.

2. If two lines meet, their point of intersection can be "found" or represented.

3. The points whose existence is given in Axiom 9 can be "found" or represented.

4. A point not on a line can be "found" or represented.

Based on the segment construction axiom, we are, in effect, making the straightedge into a ruler or, at least, into a straightedge that can be marked.   We can do this by introducing one more assumption:

[4] See Appendix, pp. 219–220.

5. Given any point A on any line, a point B can be found on either side of A such that $A-B$ is congruent to any given segment $C-D$.

With these assumptions we can now solve the following problems.[5]

Problem 1. To bisect a given angle:

Construction: *Given an angle with rays $\overrightarrow{AX}$ and $\overrightarrow{AY}$. On any side, say $\overrightarrow{AX}$, take two points, call them B and C, such that $A*B*C$. On ray $\overrightarrow{AY}$ take two points D and E such that $A*D*E$ and such that $A-D \cong A-B$, and $A-E \cong A-C$. Join $B-E$ and $D-C$ intersecting (exercise 13, Exercises 5.7) at a point F. Then $\overrightarrow{AF}$ is the bisector.*

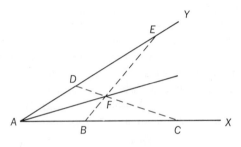

FIGURE 7.21

(Outline of) **Proof:** $\triangle BAE \cong \triangle DAC$ by SAS. By SAA (in various ways) $\triangle BFC \cong \triangle DFE$. Therefore, $B-F \cong F-D$. Then by SSS or SAS $\triangle ABF \cong \triangle ADF$. Hence, $\overrightarrow{AF}$ is the angle bisector.   ●

Problem 2. To draw a perpendicular to a given line: (Figure 7.22.)

Construction: *Let m be a line, A a point on it, and C a point not on it. Join $A-C$; take D a point on m such that $A-C \cong A-D$. Join $C-D$. Now bisect $\angle CAD$ (Problem 1); the bisector must intersect $C-D$ in a point, say G. On m take $A-F \cong A-G$. Let H be a point such that $A*G*H$ and such that $A-H \cong A-D$. Join $F-H$. The line FH is perpendicular to m.*
(Outline of) **Proof:** From triangles ACG and ADG we have $\angle AGD$ a right angle. Then, since $\triangle AGD \cong \triangle AFH$, $\angle AFH$ is a right angle; thus, FH is perpendicular to m.   ●

[5] Similar solutions can be found in books listed in the References at the end of Part II and Part III. See Halsted and Carslaw.

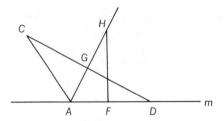

FIGURE 7.22

Problem 3. At a given point on a given line to erect the perpendicular:

Construction: *Let A be a given point on a line m. Draw a perpendicular (Problem 2) B–D to line m. If it passes through A we are through; suppose it does not, then let it intersect m in a point C such that B*C*D, and B–C ≅ C–D. Join A–B and A–D. Produce DA through A to E. Bisect ∠BAE (Problem 1) by AF. Then AF is perpendicular to m through A.*

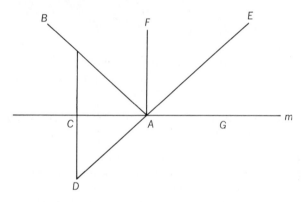

FIGURE 7.23

(Outline of) **Proof:** △ACB ≅ △ACD. Therefore, ∠BAC ≅ ∠DAC. But ∠DAC ≅ ∠EAG, (where G is a point such that C*A*G). By construction, ∠BAF ≅ ∠EAF. Thus by angle addition ∠CAF ≅ ∠GAF, and therefore AF is perpendicular to m. ●

Problem 4. From a given point not on a given line to draw the perpendicular to the line:

Construction: *Let A, B be two points on the given line and C a point not on the line. Join A–C and B–C. Take any point D on A–B and (by Problem 3) draw the perpendicular at D to A–B. By Pasch's Axiom this line must cut either A–C or B–C. Let us suppose it cuts A–C at a point E* (*if it cuts B–C the proof proceeds similarly*). Let F be a point such that $E*D*F$ and $D–E \cong D–F$. Join AF and let G be a point such that $A*F*G$ and such that $A–G \cong A–C$. Join C–G cutting (*why?*) line AB at H. Then line CH is the required perpendicular.

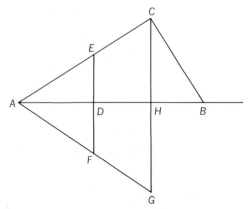

FIGURE 7.24

(*Outline of*) **Proof:** $\triangle ADE \cong \triangle ADF$; therefore $A–B$ bisects $\angle CAG$. Thus $\triangle ACH \cong \triangle AGH$, and $\angle AHC$ is a right angle, and CH is perpendicular to AB. ●

Problem 5. At a given point on a given line to make an angle congruent to a given (acute) angle:

Construction: *Let A be a point on a given line m. Let $\angle D$ be the given (acute) angle. Using Problem 4, drop a perpendicular from a point E on one side of the angle to a point on the other side; call it F. On line m take a point C such that $A–C \cong D–F$. At C erect a perpendicular to line m (Problem 3). Make $B–C \cong E–F$, and join AB. Then $\angle BAC$ is the angle to be constructed.*

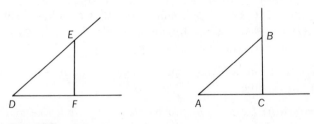

FIGURE 7.25

(*Outline of*) **Proof:** $\triangle DEF \cong \triangle ABC$. Therefore $\angle BAC \cong \angle EDF$. ●

Problem 6. To find the midpoint of a given segment:

Construction: *Let A–B be the given segment. At B erect a perpendicular to A–B (by Problem 3). On this perpendicular take any point C and join A–C. Now at B construct $\angle ABX \cong \angle CAB$ (Problem 5). Then $\overrightarrow{BX}$ must cut A–C at some point (why?), call it D. Now (Problem 1) bisect $\angle ADB$, with the bisector intersecting A–B at some point F. Then F is the midpoint of A–B.*

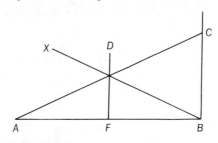

FIGURE 7.26

(*Outline of*) **Proof:** $\triangle AFD \cong \triangle BFD$. Thus $A\text{-}F \cong F\text{-}B$. (What is the purpose in constructing the right angle at B?)   ●

EXERCISES 7.5

1–5. Fill in the details left out of the constructions and proofs.

6. Use Problem 5 to construct an angle congruent to a given *obtuse* angle.

8 A Synthetic Approach
to a Metric Problem

Throughout this text we have paused to point out discrepancies and ambiguities found in the language employed by mathematicians. It has also been indicated that the meaning of a word must often be squeezed from the context if it is not to escape detection. The author has been guilty of this unfortunate practice in his use of the words "synthetic" and "metric."

Because these words have thus far been used in a nontechnical way, no formal definition has been attempted. They have, however, been used in a traditional manner. Traditionally, the word "synthetic" is used to name ("describe" is hardly an adequate word) the approach to geometry first employed by Euclid and later used by many others. The word does not refer to a deductive system as such, but, rather—if the meaning of the word can be said to have any characterizing features at all—to such a system when it is developed without the use of numbers. Contrasted to this is the "analytic" or "coordinate" approach. Also in contrast to the synthetic approach is a "metric" approach, in which one does employ numbers, and uses them to define real-valued functions (distance, and angular measure) in terms of which the concepts of congruence and between can then be defined. The metric approach is of comparatively recent origin.

To further confuse the issue, the word "metric" has other uses in mathematics today. In at least one of these uses many of the properties introduced in this text would be regarded as "metric" properties, even if numbers were not employed. In this second sense, there can be an "analytic" geometry which is not a "metric" geometry. Discussions of "descriptive" versus "metric" properties of geometry, as those words are used to distinguish the properties of projective geometry from nonprojective geometry, can be found in some books on projective geometry.

Regardless of one's interpretation of "metric," there still remain two theorems of Euclid's first twenty-eight that we shall need and have not yet proved; we are not yet able to do so precisely because of their "metric" characteristics.

The purpose of this chapter is threefold: to explain why these theorems have not yet been proved, to introduce an important new concept which will help us to prove them, and to prove them.

8.1 Difficulties in Some Simple Theorems

Given that a statement is phraseable in the language of a system, then no matter how simple it is, no matter how evident its truth, if it is not an axiom or definition it should, if possible, be proved as a theorem. We say "if possible" and thereby introduce two interesting ramifications.

On the one hand, even when a statement can be expressed in the language of a system, it may not always be possible to prove or disprove it. Several examples of this situation were given in Chapters 2 and 3 in reference to Axiom Systems 1, 2, and 3. In the examples given it was literally not possible to prove or disprove certain statements. It was explained that the existence of this situation is closely related to the concept of completeness of an axiomatic system, a concept that introduces complex problems in logic.

On the other hand, there are many instances in mathematics where proofs have simply not been forthcoming. A classic example of this is Goldbach's conjecture that "Every even integer (except 2) is the sum of two primes." This statement has never been proved, even though there is a great deal of empirical evidence in its favor. Another famous theorem first suggested by empirical evidence but never proved is the famous four-color problem: that no matter how many countries a map contains it is possible to color it, using only four colors, in such a manner that no two countries with a border in common have the same color.

In the history of mathematics there exist many statements of utmost simplicity whose proofs have escaped the concentrated efforts of scores of mathematicians. There are also many statements of utmost simplicity whose proofs, when found, have turned out to be extremely complicated.

An excellent illustration of this is the Jordan-curve theorem. It is quite obvious that a simple closed curve partitions the plane into three sets: the curve, an inside, and an outside. This fact had been used for centuries. It was so intuitively evident that no one thought it necessary to prove it until the last century. When the attempt finally was made by Camille Jordan (1838–1922), the proof not only was complicated but contained errors. It was some time before rigorous proofs of the theorem were found, and then (for the general simple closed curve) they were of a degree of difficulty beyond the level of this text.

Interesting as they may be, these discussions of the difficulties inherent in the proofs of many simple theorems are presented primarily to set the stage for the Euclidean theorem:

In any triangle, two sides taken together in any manner are greater than the remaining one.

In a minor way, this theorem illustrates the points considered in the preceding paragraphs.

Consider first its simplicity. The ancient Epicureans ridiculed the proof of this theorem. They said that the statement is so simple, so clear and obvious, that it does not require proof. They contended that even a dumb animal knows that the theorem is true; for if food is placed on a vertex of a triangle, and the animal on another vertex, it will never walk two sides of the triangle to get the food. As picturesque as this criticism is, it is quite irrelevant; unless the statement is taken as an axiom it requires proof.

Now consider its degree of difficulty. It is rather astonishing that after proving ninety-nine theorems, all of which have to do with the same general subject matter as that covered in the first twenty-eight theorems of the *Elements*, we have not yet proved two of the latter. Nor are we yet in a position to do so. What is it that is so difficult about the proof of such a theorem? Let us see how Euclid handles it.

Proposition 20. In any triangle, two sides taken together in any manner are greater than the remaining one.

For let ABC be a triangle; I say that in the triangle ABC two sides taken together in any manner are greater than the remaining one, namely

BA, AC greater than BC,

AB, BC greater than AC,

BC, CA greater than AB.

For let BA be drawn through to the point D, let DA be made equal to CA, and let DC be joined. (see Figure 8.1.)

Then, since DA is equal to AC, the angle ADC is also equal to the angle ACD; therefore, the angle BCD is greater than the angle ADC.

And, since DCB is a triangle having the angle BCD greater than the angle BDC, and the greater angle is subtended by the greater side, therefore, DB is greater than BC.

But DA is equal to AC; therefore, BA, AC are greater than BC.

Similarly we can prove that AB, BC are also greater than CA, and BC, CA than AB.

Therefore, etc.   Q.E.D.

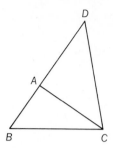

FIGURE 8.1

At first glance, this proof does not appear difficult at all. It merely uses theorems that have already been developed. But is this the case? A more careful look shows that a problem exists even before the proof is reached; it exists in stating the theorem. For what does it mean to say "two sides taken together"?

Similarly, in the proof itself, what does it mean to say "*BA, AC* are greater than *BC*"? In both cases, are we not really talking about addition of line segments? And, if so, can one avoid the problem of what is to be meant by "addition" by simply avoiding the use of the word? Obviously, no.

Furthermore, in the proof of the theorem, how does one justify going from "*DB* is greater than *BC*" to "*BA, AC* are greater than *BC*"? It is evident that to justify this step one needs a new theorem:

(a) If $a = b$, and $a + c > d$, then $b + c > d$

But how is such a theorem to be proved or even stated in a synthetic manner?

It might be argued with some cogency that, if the truth of a statement is so obvious and its proof so difficult, it could just as well be made an axiom, especially since there has been no attempt in this system to keep the number of axioms to a minimum. However, this would be of little help, for there are many difficulties intertwined. There would still be a need for a definition of addition; also, to make the statement an axiom would not provide a means for proving statements such as (a), which are useful in themselves; and, finally, it would not help us to prove the theorem that follows or solve the problems that *it* raises.

Proposition 17. In any triangle two angles taken together in any manner are less than two right angles.

Let *ABC* be a triangle; I say that two angles of the triangle *ABC* taken together in any manner are less than two right angles.

For let *BC* be produced to *D*.

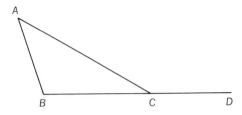

FIGURE 8.2

Then, since the angle ACD is an exterior angle of the triangle ABC, it is greater than the interior and opposite angle ABC.

Let the angle ACB be added to each; therefore, the angles ACD, ACB are greater than the angles ABC, BCA. But the angles ACD, ACB are equal to two right angles.

Therefore, the angles ABC, BCA are less than two right angles.

Similarly, we can prove that the angles BAC, ACB are also less than two right angles, and so are the angles CAB, ABC as well.

Therefore, etc.   Q.E.D.

Here we raise two new but related problems. The first one once again has to do with the statement of the theorem. It can be solved by introducing a definition: any two angles $\angle A$ and $\angle B$ are said to be *taken together less than two right angles* if and only if adjacent angles congruent to $\angle A$ and $\angle B$, respectively, do not form a linear pair *but do form a new angle.*

The other problem arises in the proof and gives rise to the need for a theorem analogous to the following:

(b) If $a < b$, then $a + c < b + c$.

Because of the nature of these problems they cannot merely be solved by introducing new axioms. If we were going to become very deeply involved with concepts of this sort, our only recourse would be to introduce a number system. This is the easiest, most expedient way to handle such problems. Once again, however, we are going to avoid the easiest way.

Having come so far without one, it seems a shame to introduce a number system to prove theorems that will be used infrequently. However, without an adequate alternative this is not sufficient reason for avoiding such a system. Our alternative is not only adequate but also instructive, for in order to avoid introducing a number system we shall introduce a concept useful to almost every branch of pure mathematics. This is the concept of an *equivalence class.*

8.2 Measure

We have frequently encountered relations that are reflexive, symmetric, and transitive. In Chapter 5 a definition was given that says that any relation satisfying these three properties is called an equivalence relation. Instead of introducing this concept as a definition, it would have been possible to consider the three statements given in the definition as axioms. It then would have been possible to derive some of the properties common to equivalence relations.

It would have been found that any equivalence relation in a given set divides the set into disjoint subsets. These subsets are such that their union is the entire set and any two elements of one subset are equivalent. In fact, two elements are equivalent if and only if they belong to the same subset.

As an example from algebra, consider the set S of nonnegative integers $\{0, 1, 2, 3, 4, \cdot \cdot \cdot\}$ and the equivalence relation E, where two elements x, y, are related, written xEy, if and only if division of x, y, by 3 leaves the same remainder. This relation divides the set S into the following sets, called *equivalence classes*:

$$[0] = \{0, 3, 6, 9, \cdot \cdot \cdot\}$$
$$[1] = \{1, 4, 7, 10, \cdot \cdot \cdot\}$$
$$[2] = \{2, 5, 8, 11, \cdot \cdot \cdot\}$$

It should be noted that these sets are disjoint, that their union is the entire set, and that two elements are equivalent if and only if they belong to the same set. In other words, the set of equivalence classes in a set S form a partition of S.

The converse of this statement is also true. That is, given sets S_1, S_2, $\cdot \cdot \cdot S_n$, which form a partition of a set S, then they define an equivalence relation R on S, where xRy if and only if x and y belong to the same S_i. The reader should verify that this does form an equivalence relation and might do well to pursue the subject further on his own.

The foregoing should enable one to understand the significance of the following definition:

Definition 43. The *measure* of a line segment $A-B$ is the *set* of all line segments congruent to $A-B$.

Notation Rule 17. *The measure of a line segment $A-B$ will be denoted by:*

$$m(A-B)$$

It now follows that $A-B \cong C-D$ if and only if $m(A-B) = m(C-D)$; and, if $m(A-B) \neq m(C-D)$, then the sets are disjoint. In other words, the measure of a line segment is an equivalence class.

It remains to be seen how this concept will help to define addition of segments and angles.

8.3   Addition of Line Segments

To be able to add nonconsecutive noncollinear line segments we will have to define addition in terms of the measure of the line segments, in terms of equivalence classes. In order to be able to do this we must be sure that the definition is a sound one, that it does not depend on the particular member of the equivalence class chosen but on the class itself. This point may require more explanation.

We know that if $A-B$ and $C-D$ are any two segments then there exist points X, Y, Z such that $X*Y*Z$ and $A-B \cong X-Y$, and $C-D \cong Y-Z$. That this is so follows from the axioms on segments. Furthermore, it follows from the segment addition axiom that all such segments $X-Z$ are congruent. From this and the properties of the equivalence relation "$\cong$" it follows that the equivalence class $m(X-Z)$ is independent of the choice of X, Y, Z and that it depends upon $m(A-B)$ and $m(C-D)$ rather than the particular segments $A-B$ and $C-D$. We can now present the following definition with assurance that the definition makes sense.

Definition 44. $m(A-B) + m(C-D)$ means $m(X-Z)$ where $X-Z$ is a line segment such that a point Y exists with $X*Y*Z$ and $A-B \cong X-Y$ and $C-D \cong Y-Z$.

From the substitution theorems 58 and 59 it is known that if $A-B < C-D$, then any segment in $m(A-B)$ is less than any segment in $m(C-D)$. So the following definition may be stated:

Definition 45. $m(A-B) < m(C-D)$ means that every segment congruent to $A-B$ is less than every segment congruent to $C-D$.

With these definitions it is now possible to state and prove the following theorems:

Theorem 100. If $m(C-D) < m(E-F)$, then $m(A-B) + m(C-D) < m(A-B) + m(E-F)$.

Proof: $m(A-B) + m(C-D)$ means $m(X-Z)$ where $X-Z$ is a line segment such that there exists a Y and $X*Y*Z$ and $A-B \cong X-Y$ and $C-D \cong Y-Z$.

$m(A-B) + m(E-F)$ means $m(X-W)$ where $X-W$ is a line segment such that there exists a V and $X*V*W$ and $A-B \cong X-V$ and $E-F \cong V-W$. Now by the segment construction axiom, $Y = V$, so

$$A-B \cong X-Y \text{ and } E-F \cong Y-W$$

Thus, to show $m(A-B) + m(C-D) < m(A-B) + m(E-F)$ is to show

$$m(X-Z) < m(X-W)$$

But $m(X-Z) < m(X-W)$ iff there exists a point M such that $X-Z \cong X-M$ and $X*M*W$.

Now, since it was given that $m(C-D) < m(E-F)$, and since it was established that $C-D \cong Y-Z$ and that $E-F \cong Y-W$, it follows that $Y-Z < Y-W$ and hence that there exists a point M such that $Y*M*W$ and $Y-Z \cong Y-M$. It will then follow that $Z = M$ from the segment construction axiom. Thus, by substitution, $Y*Z*W$.

It is now the case that $Y*Z*W$ and $X*Y*Z$; it thus follows from Theorem 9 that $X*Z*W$. Thus, by definition, $X-Z < X-W$; $m(X-Z) < m(X-W)$; and, finally, $m(A-B) + m(C-D) < m(A-B) + m(E-F)$. ●

It readily follows in similar manner that:

Theorem 101. If $m(C-D) < m(E-F)$, then $m(C-D) + m(A-B) < m(E-F) + m(A-B)$.

We could now go back and prove each of the inequality theorems for line segments over again for the *measure* of line segments. But this is not necessary; the main use we shall make of the concept of measure is in adding nonadjacent line segments and nonadjacent angles. Let us assume where necessary that the preceding theorems on inequalities are stated in the proper terms and concern ourselves with the theorems requiring *addition*.

Theorem 102. If $m(A-B) < m(C-D)$ and $m(E-F) < m(G-H)$, then $m(A-B) + m(E-F) < m(C-D) + m(G-H)$.

Proof: By Theorem 101, if $m(A-B) < m(C-D)$, then it may be concluded that $m(A-B) + m(E-F) < m(C-D) + m(E-F)$.

By Theorem 100, if $m(E-F) < m(G-H)$, then it may be concluded that $m(C-D) + m(E-F) < m(C-D) + m(G-H)$.

Hence, by substitution and transitivity the conclusion follows. ●

We can now prove Euclid's Theorem 20. Instead of merely correcting the proof as it was given, a task made easy by the developments just presented, we shall present an alternative proof:

Theorem 103. In any triangle, two sides taken together in any manner are greater than the remaining side.

Restatement: *Given triangle ABC, prove that:*

$$m(B-C) < m(A-B) + m(A-C)$$
$$m(A-C) < m(A-B) + m(B-C)$$
$$m(A-B) < m(B-C) + m(A-C)$$

Proof: The proof of any one of the inequalities is the same. Let us prove the first.

Let $A-D$ be the bisector of $\angle BAC$, meeting $B-C$ in point D. Thus, $B*D*C$.

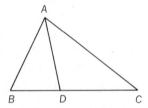

FIGURE 8.3

Then, in triangle ADC, $\angle ADB$ is an exterior angle; thus by Theorem 79 $\angle DAC < \angle ADB$.

But $\angle DAC \cong \angle BAD$; thus by Theorem 67 $\angle BAD < \angle ADB$. It then follows from Theorem 82 that $B-D < A-B$.

By similar reasoning we can show that $C-D < A-C$.

Hence, from Theorem 102 (and definitions about measure), it follows that:

$$m(B-D) + m(C-D) < m(A-B) + m(A-C)$$

or

$$m(B-C) < m(A-B) + m(A-C). \quad \bullet$$

8.4   Addition of Angles

Altering the hypothesis of a theorem obviously not only changes the theorem but has a varying effect on the system in which the theorem occurs. In order to understand the significance of a theorem, it is often illuminating to discard parts of its hypothesis and study the effects of these changes on theorems to be derived from it; changes may also have to be made in theorems immediately preceding it. Such exploratory examination usually gives new insight into the strengths and weaknesses of the original theorem. The same can be said for altering the definitions and concepts of a system.

If no other benefit comes from the discussion in this chapter, perhaps it will help to give the reader new understanding of topics that, when studied using numbers, seemed trivial. After all, it must be remembered that number systems are a relatively recent invention; as we know them today, they were nonexistent in Euclid's time. This is certainly a major reason that so much more has been accomplished in mathematics and the sciences in the past few centuries than in all the rest of man's recorded history. But to understand the real significance of something that has become so much a part of us we must see what happens when we are forced to do without it. For example, we might try to find a reasonable facsimile.

Those familiar with the "new math" will realize that ordinary numbers can be represented as equivalence classes, not too unlike the one introduced here as the measure of a set. If various laws of addition were introduced one would come even closer to considering the measure of a set as a number. For example, a *commutative* law might be introduced (thereby making it unnecessary to prove Theorem 101); it might also be stressed that the sum of the measures of two segments is the measure of a segment or, in other words, that the set of measures is *closed* under addition. It seems that such a development would not lead to any problems.

When we consider properties of angles, however, new difficulties arise. As already explained, there has been no mention of straight angles in this text; and, following Euclid, angles greater than a straight angle have not been introduced. Therefore, the set of measures for angles cannot be closed under addition. Nor will it always be the case that the sum of the measures of two angles is the measure of an angle.

To attempt to repair this by introducing the needed angles would upset much of the material so far developed, for we would have to define what is meant by the interior of a straight angle and by the interior of an angle greater than a straight angle. The reader might consider how much of the theory in this text depends on having the interior of an angle precisely defined.

Rather than think about such an immense problem now, we shall restrict the following definitions and theorems.

First we shall introduce the definition of measure:

Definition 46. The *measure* of an angle $\angle AOB$ is the *set* of all angles congruent to $\angle AOB$.

Notation Rule 18. *The measure of an angle $\angle AOB$ will be denoted by:*

$$m(\angle AOB)$$

As in the case of segments, it now follows that the measure of an angle is an equivalence class.

In order to make any sense from the definitions and theorems that follow it will be necessary to define what is meant by the *existence* of a sum as well as what is meant by the *sum*. Which definition should come first is a moot point.

Definition 47. $m(\angle AOB) + m(\angle CO'D)$ (if it exists), means m ($\angle EO''F$) where $\angle EO''F$ is an angle such that a point G exists interior to $\angle EO''F$ and such that $\angle AOB \cong \angle EO''G$ and $\angle CO'D \cong \angle GO''F$.

Definition 48. The sum, defined in Definition 47, is said to *exist* iff there exist adjacent angles $\angle EO''G$, $\angle GO''F$ with the following property:

If $\overrightarrow{O''G}$ is the common side of the adjacent angles, then $\overrightarrow{O''G}$ and $\overrightarrow{O''F}$ are on the same side (half plane) of line $O''E$; and, $\overrightarrow{O''G}$ and $\overrightarrow{O''E}$ are on the same side of line $O''F$.

A diagram should be drawn to see if this definition fulfills the prerequisites that intuition says it should. The definition should say that the sum of two obtuse angles cannot exist, that the sum of two right angles cannot exist, and that the sum of an obtuse angle and acute angle can exist only under certain conditions.

Definition 49. $m(\angle AOB) < m(\angle CO'D)$ means that any angle congruent to $\angle AOB$ is less than any angle congruent to $\angle CO'D$.

That these definitions are meaningful follows from Theorems 64, 67, and 68. Using the definitions, we can prove the following theorems in a manner analogous to the proofs of Theorems 100, 101, and 102 respectively.

Theorem 104. If $m(\angle DEF) < m(\angle GHI)$ then, if the sums exist, $m(\angle ABC) + m(\angle DEF) < m(\angle ABC) + m(\angle GHI)$.

Proof: Left as an exercise.

Theorem 105. If $m(\angle DEF) < m(\angle GHI)$ then, if the sums exist, $m(\angle DEF) + m(\angle ABC) < m(\angle GHI) + m(\angle ABC)$.

Proof: Left as an exercise.

Theorem 106. If $m(\angle ABC) < m(\angle DEF)$ and $m(\angle GHI) < m(\angle JKL)$ then, if the sums exist, $m(\angle ABC) + m(\angle GHI) < m(\angle DEF) + m(\angle JKL)$.

Proof: Left as an exercise.

We have presented these theorems here because there will be one or two occasions to use them in the next two chapters. It is ironic, however, that even these theorems are not of much assistance in proving Euclid's Proposition 17. Even now we shall have to resort to a proof that seems artificial. The reason for this is that we do not have straight angles; furthermore, even if we had straight angles, it would still be necessary to assume or prove statements to the effect that any angle congruent to a straight angle is a straight angle and that all straight angles are congruent. It would also be necessary to define exactly what it means for an angle to be less than a straight angle.

The following proof does not solve these problems; it avoids them.

Language Rule 16: *If the sum of two angles exists, the two angles are said to be* TAKEN TOGETHER LESS THAN TWO RIGHT ANGLES.

Theorem 107. In any triangle two angles taken together in any manner are less than two right angles.

Proof: Let ABC be a triangle with $B*C*D$. Then since $\angle ACD$ is an exterior angle of the triangle, $\angle ABC < \angle ACD$. Then $\angle ABC$ and $\angle BCA$,

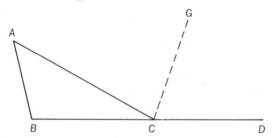

FIGURE 8.4

taken together are less than two right angles because, since $\angle ABC < \angle ACD$, there exists a point G interior to $\angle ACD$ and such that $\angle ACG \cong \angle ABC$.

It is the case that $\angle BCA$ and $\angle ACG$ satisfy the conditions in Definition 48. Therefore, when stated in the language of Definition 47 and 48, and Language Rule 16, the conclusion follows.

A similar argument carries through for any two angles. ●

EXERCISES 8.4

1. Prove Theorem 104. (Hint: analogous to proof of Theorem 100 using Theorem 51b.)

2. Prove Theorem 105.
3. Prove Theorem 106.

8.5   Epilogue

We have now concluded Part II; Part III will introduce a geometry that will be a continuation of what we have started and yet a new geometry with strange new properties. Because of this it might help the reader if we explain why, having started a development that is well on the way to producing the familiar properties of Euclidean geometry, we should bring it to such an abrupt end. We should also explain the alternatives.

It should be fairly evident that there are not exactly 107 theorems that can be proved in the axiomatic system we have presented, that the system does not die a natural death at Theorem 107. On the contrary, without the addition of another axiom, an infinite number of theorems provable in the system remain. Many of these might be quite trivial and useless, but others would be significant and useful. Some of these will be stated in Chapter 10, where it will be explained why they have been postponed until then.

Thus we might continue with the present axiomatic system. As another alternative, we might attempt to move further along the lines of elementary Euclidean geometry. To do so, one of the first things we might do is to introduce the Euclidean parallel axiom, namely, that through a point not on a given line, only one line exists parallel to the given line. From this the theory about parallelograms readily follows.

We might then introduce a continuity axiom and a number system and develop the theory of similarity and areas. The circle might be introduced and its properties derived—including all the theorems about chords and tangents presented in high school geometry texts and many properties not introduced there. Still other axioms might be introduced (see *Foundations of Geometry* by Hilbert) sufficient to derive the theory of Euclidean three-space.

Within this framework exist countless theorems old and new. Some of them would be familiar, others would not. Some, such as those concerned with the very recent theory of convex bodies, were never dreamed of by Euclid, although they belong to Euclidean geometry. Thus we could follow a path leading deeply into the heart of Euclidean geometry, but that is not what we are going to do.

We shall introduce only one more axiom and it will not be one of those already mentioned. Instead we shall introduce a negation of the parallel axiom and investigate the path it opens. It will no doubt be a strange one;

but it should prove to be interesting and instructive. Indeed, it is hoped that it will give the reader far more insight into contemporary mathematics than would be gained from pursuing Euclidean geometry at this elementary level.

references

Birkhoff, G. D., and Ralph Beatley. *Basic Geometry*. Chicago: Scott, Foresman and Co., 1940.

Brumfiel, C. F., R. E. Eicholz, and M. E. Shanks. *Geometry*. Reading, Massachusetts: Addison-Wesley Publishing Co., Inc., 1960.

Forder, H. G. *The Foundations of Euclidean Geometry*. New York: Cambridge University Press, 1927. Reprinted by Dover Publications, Inc., 1958.

Halsted, G. B. *Rational Geometry*. New York: John Wiley and Sons, Inc., 1904.

Heath, T. L. *The Thirteen Books of Euclid's Elements*, 2d ed., vol. 1. New York: Cambridge University Press, 1926. Reprinted by Dover Publications, Inc., 1956.

Hilbert, David. *The Foundations of Geometry*. Translated by E. J. Townsend. Chicago: The Open Court Publishing Company, 1902.

Moise, E. E. *Elementary Geometry From an Advanced Standpoint*. Reading, Massachusetts: Addison-Wesley Publishing Co., Inc., 1963.

Prenowitz, W., and M. Jordan. *Basic Concepts of Geometry*. New York: Blaisdell Publishing Company, 1965.

School Mathematics Study Group. *Mathematics for High School, Geometry*, parts 1 and 2. New Haven, Connecticut: School Mathematics Study Group, 1959.

part 3

Non-Euclidean

Geometry

introduction

That, if a straight line falling on two straight lines makes the interior angles on the same side less than two right angles, the two straight lines, if produced indefinitely, meet on that side on which are the angles less than the two right angles.[1]

Euclid presented this statement as his fifth postulate (axiom) and thereby profoundly influenced the course of mathematical history. Although historians disagree about the authenticity of many parts of the *Elements*, they usually agree that this statement originated with Euclid. That he placed it among his assumptions rather than introducing it as a theorem must be considered a monument to his genius.

It is possible that outside of this text the reader has never before seen this statement and is, therefore, somewhat confused as to how or why it is such an important one. It may help if we say that this statement is known

---

[1] Whenever we wish to refer to this particular statement we shall call it the *Parallel Postulate,* or the *Fifth.*

as Euclid's Parallel Postulate; on the other hand, this may cause more bewilderment, for most readers undoubtedly conceive of a parallel axiom along such lines as: through a point not on a given line exactly one line exists parallel to the given line. Indeed, it turns out that this statement is equivalent to the one quoted above. But had Euclid made his statement in the more familiar form it might never have played such an important historical role.

It should be remembered that at the time of Euclid and for centuries thereafter a postulate was regarded not merely as a truth but as a self-evident truth, a truth beyond doubt. Even today this notion is widely held, as indicated by the definitions found in any standard dictionary and by the fact that many people still regard mathematics as the absolute science. This opinion was held all the more firmly in ancient times, and thus incited attacks upon the Fifth.

A look at the other postulates[2] of the *Elements* helps one to understand why the Fifth might cause such furor. Not only is it much more complicated, not only is it not self-evident, it is actually open to doubt.

It was argued that the truth of the Fifth is, at best, merely plausible. For, the arguments continued, is it not true that there exist "lines" which are asymptotic—as in the hyperbola and conchoid? And does not the fact that some lines exist which, though converging, do not meet no matter how far extended make it open to question whether the same might not be true of straight lines? If so, if open to question, then the statement cannot be a postulate.

Centuries of trying to prove the Fifth from the other postulates followed. These attempts led to the development of new geometries and to an entirely new and vastly richer approach to mathematics in general. Exactly how this came about, and a discussion of some of the results, will be the subject of the rest of the text.

[2] See Appendix, pp. 218–219.

9 The Concept of Parallelism

In discussing some of the attempts to prove Euclid's fifth postulate we shall learn that there are many statements equivalent to the Fifth. A survey of a list of such statements should convince the reader that the Parallel Postulate is rich in implications. He may wonder, therefore, what would occur if such a statement were discarded or negated. What would happen if we introduced a new parallel postulate? This will be seen in this chapter.

9.1 History

Although we shall not review the entire history of attempts to prove the Fifth,[1] it is necessary to discuss some of these attempts in order to learn how they have led to new discoveries. It is hoped that the following presentation will provide some answers and induce the reader to seek out others.

Proclus (410–485 A.D.)

Proclus is the source of much of the knowledge we have about Euclid and his earliest critics and commentators. According to Proclus, the first attempts to prove the Parallel Postulate began almost immediately and were coordinated with revised statements of Euclid's definition of *parallel*. One should not confuse the postulate with his twenty-third definition:

[1] For a more complete history, see R. Bonola, *Non-Euclidean Geometry*, translated by H. S. Carslaw (Open Court Publishing Company, 1912).

Parallel straight lines are straight lines which, being in the same plane and being produced indefinitely in both directions, do not meet one another in either direction.

Of the many attempts listed by Proclus, the most significant involves changing this definition of parallel lines to: parallel lines are lines which are everywhere equidistant. How this is then used to attempt to prove the Fifth need not be discussed. For Proclus was the first to point out that there *might* exist parallel lines in Euclid's sense that are not everywhere equidistant. Thus, to use his definition, it would be necessary to prove first that if two straight lines do not meet they are equidistant. And to do this requires the Fifth Postulate or a statement equivalent to it.

As is often the case, the good critic is not necessarily an innovator. The barbs Proclus throws at the attempts of others are sharp and well-directed; but, when he tries a proof of his own, he falls equally short of success.

First, he argues that the Fifth cannot be an axiom. His reasoning, if accurately recorded, must be taken as evidence of how distorted man's thinking can become when he is obsessed with proving a point. Proclus argues, correctly, that Proposition 17 of the *Elements* is the converse of the Fifth; but he then says that it is impossible that a statement whose converse can be proved is not capable itself of being proved!(!)(!)

With reasoning such as this to justify his attempt, he then proves the Fifth by assuming a statement equivalent to it, namely, that parallel lines remain a finite distance apart.

It is for this type of argument that Proclus criticizes all others who had attempted a proof. In each case he points out that, to prove the postulate, either an assumption equivalent to it or some paradoxical assumption about infinite areas and lengths behaving like finite ones has been made. This criticism applies equally well to most later attempts.

Through the ages, in the many attempts to prove the Parallel Postulate, a long list of statements equivalent to it has been gathered. Most of the important ones were known to Proclus. Among them are the following:

1. There exist straight lines everywhere equidistant from one another.
2. If a straight line intersects one of two parallels, it will intersect the other.
3. Straight lines parallel to the same straight line are parallel to one another.
4. The sum of the angles of a triangle is equal to two right angles.
5. Two straight lines which intersect one another cannot both be parallel to the same line.

6. Through a given point not on a given line only one line can exist parallel to the given line.

Statement (6) is probably the form in which most readers have encountered the parallel postulate. Although known to Proclus, it is called "Playfair's Axiom" after a British geometer of the eighteenth century.

When we say that these statements are each equivalent to the Fifth we mean that they (together with other assumptions) mutually imply each other. That the Parallel Postulate implies each of these statements is evident to anyone who has studied the *Elements*, for these statements are either proved there as theorems or follow quite directly from theorems that are proved. That each of these statements in turn imply the Fifth has been shown at various times by many mathematicians; some of the proofs are quite complicated, but this should come as no surprise since, after all, it requires thirty theorems before Euclid proves any of them from the Fifth.

If we were merely attempting to prove the Parallel Postulate as a theorem in some system, there would be nothing wrong with using any of these equivalent assumptions in proving the Fifth. Because we are attempting to prove the Parallel Postulate from the other four postulates of Euclid, care must be taken. Suppose, for example, that we use the fact that the sum of the angles of a triangle is equal to two right angles to prove the Fifth, and suppose the proof is correct. The problem with such a course lies in determining whether or not the assumed statement about the sum of the angles is a true statement. It is either an axiom or a theorem. To take it as an axiom defeats the purpose of the undertaking. To take it as a theorem involves one in a circularity problem, for the only way to prove it is to use the Fifth or a statement equivalent to it.

Gerolamo Saccheri (1667–1733)

During the centuries that followed Proclus, countless other attempts were made to prove the Parallel Postulate and numerous new flaws and equivalent statements were uncovered. We shall pass over these attempts until we come to Gerolamo Saccheri, an Italian mathematician of the seventeenth and eighteenth centuries, who came up with a new approach.

Saccheri assumes the first four postulates, all the theorems proved from them (the first 28), and assumes that the Fifth is false. In other words, he attempts to prove the truth of the postulate by the indirect method.

As a basic figure in his work, he takes a quadrilateral $ABCD$, with right angles at A and B, and A–$D \cong B$–C. He then proves that the angles at C and D must be congruent to each other and goes on to consider three hypotheses:

1. $\angle C$ and $\angle D$ are right angles.
2. $\angle C$ and $\angle D$ are obtuse angles.
3. $\angle C$ and $\angle D$ are acute angles.

He proves that if any one of these hypotheses is true for a single quadrilateral it is true for every quadrilateral; he also proves that depending upon whether hypothesis 1, 2, or 3 is assumed the sum of the angles of a triangle will be, respectively, equal to, greater than, or less than two right angles. He then goes on to' show that on assuming the second hypothesis a contradiction is reached, and therefore the assumption must be discarded. To complete his argument, he attempts to eliminate the third hypothesis by assuming it is true.

To state all the theorems he derives under this assumption would needlessly repeat many of the theorems of the remaining sections of this book. Rather, let it be pointed out that instead of trusting to logic, Saccheri, predisposed to find a contradiction, finds one after a circuitous search located at a point at infinity—a point, needless to say, that causes a great deal of trouble.

Saccheri himself was not satisfied with the "contradiction" he reached and tried other methods, most of which had been tried many times over the centuries. If he had placed more faith in his reasoning and less faith in his faith, he would have been credited with the discovery of non-Euclidean geometry a hundred years before it was finally discovered. As it was, his work was soon forgotten and more or less remained so until it was resurrected late in the nineteenth century.

Johann H. Lambert (1728–1777)

Johann Lambert, a Swiss mathematician of the eighteenth century, was probably aware of Saccheri's work. His method of approach is quite similar except that, instead of a figure with two right angles, he starts out with a figure with three right angles. He, too, considers three hypotheses; all are about the nature of the fourth angle:

1. The fourth angle is a right angle.
2. The fourth angle is obtuse.
3. The fourth angle is acute.

On assuming the second hypothesis he easily obtains a contradiction. But once again in assuming the hypothesis of the acute angle a contradiction does not easily follow; however, he does reach several new conclusions. He proves, as did Saccheri, that the sum of the angles of any triangle is less than two right angles (the amount of the difference they call the *defect*); but, he goes a step further than Saccheri and proves that the defect of any polygon is *proportional to the area* of the polygon.

Furthermore, he comes up with still more astounding information, namely, that under this hypothesis there would be an *absolute unit of measure*. We shall discuss this concept later.

Once again, however, intuition takes precedence over logic and Lambert concludes that, since there can be no absolute unit of measure, this hypothesis must be false.

Gauss, Bolyai, Lobachevsky

Attacks on the Parallel Postulate continued and, indeed, grew more intense until the early 1820s. At that time a subtle change in outlook and objective became discernable among some of the mathematicians concerned with the problem.

In Germany, Carl Friederich Gauss (1777–1855) had been bringing his great gifts to bear upon the problem for some time. It was unfortunate for his contemporaries that he did not publish his findings. In letters to his friends, made public after his death, he expressly asked them not to reveal his findings while he lived. In these letters one discovers that he had gone a long way toward discovering and developing some of the properties of a new geometry that he called *non-Euclidean*. It is probable that he was the first to use this name.

Although it may never be known exactly what motivated him to keep his findings secret, it is likely that fear for his reputation may have been a factor. For, on the one hand, Gauss was recognized in his own lifetime as one of the greatest of mathematicians. On the other hand, he was aware that his discoveries would be shocking to layman and mathematician alike; indeed, they ran so counter to one's intuition that devulging them might have opened him to ridicule. At the same time, keeping his work secret meant that he never received the honor that might have been his due; the credit must go instead to the son of a friend of his and a young contemporary.

In Hungary, Johan Bolyai (1802–1860), and in Russia, Nicolai Ivanovich Lobachevsky (1793–1856) had each been working on the problem from 1820–1830. At the end of the decade they finally published their findings; ironically, it did not create any great stir and neither man achieved any fame for his accomplishment during his lifetime. Gauss read Bolyai's work within a year of publication and was pleased with it; he became aware of Lobachevsky's work somewhat later and was equally impressed. However, his praise was limited to correspondence with his friends and thus his immense prestige did nothing toward making either work known or accepted.

Instead of being pleased by Gauss's praise, Bolyai was disappointed and suspicious. He knew that his father and Gauss had corresponded for years; he had written his father of his discoveries in great detail years before they were finally published. Therefore, when Gauss praised his work but added that it was of the same kind that he himself had been working on, Bolyai felt that Gauss was attempting to gain credit for his own discovery.

According to the best historical detective work, each of the three men was ignorant of what the other was doing. It is not at all uncommon in the history of mathematics and the sciences for discoveries to be made simultaneously by different men, in scattered places, each ignorant of the others' work. It would seem that when an idea is ripe it will be forthcoming.

The work of Gauss, Bolyai, and Lobachevsky will be analyzed in detail as we continue.

B. Riemann (1826–1866)

The next great breakthrough occurred in 1854. Riemann, a student of Gauss and later one of the great mathematicians of his time, presented a paper in which he made a distinction between the infinitude of a line and its unboundedness. We have had occasion to refer to this before in regard to Euclid's Proposition 16, the exterior angle theorem. Let us recapitulate.

Suppose we consider a line drawn around a sphere, that is, a circle. It is not infinite in length; it has a definite circumference. Yet it is unbounded in the sense that we can continue around it without stop. Suppose now that we not only contradict the Parallel Postulate but also the assumption that lines are of infinite length. What happens then?

Because no one had considered this before the time of Riemann, no one had observed that in Saccheri's and Lambert's work the reason that the hypothesis of the obtuse angle leads to a contradiction is that they both assume that lines are of infinite length. If this assumption had not been made they would have reached no contradiction in pursuing the hypothesis of the obtuse angle.

Riemann suggested such a geometry, a geometry in which there are no parallel lines, lines may enclose a space, and the sum of the angles of a triangle is greater than two right angles. Unfortunately, the techniques needed to deal adequately with a discussion of Riemann's suggested geometry are beyond the limited scope of this text.

Felix Klein (1849–1925)

Work related to still another type of geometry developed in the nineteenth century, projective geometry, led Klein to classify the subject into three types: parabolic, elliptic, and hyperbolic geometry. They correspond respectively to the geometry of Euclid, Riemann, and Bolyai-Lobachevsky. The classifications are commonly used today.

In 1871 Klein pointed out that there are really two types of Riemann geometry. There is the spherical type in which two straight lines have two points in common and the elliptic type where two straight lines have but one point in common; because of the intersection properties of lines, these two geometries are often classified according to Klein's scheme as double-elliptic and single-elliptic respectively.

This discovery of Klein's helps us to solve the problem raised in Chapter 7 concerning the proof of the exterior angle theorem. It will be recalled that to prove that theorem we first had to prove Theorem 75, that through a point outside a given line there exists at least one parallel. This statement is consistent with both Euclidean and Bolyai-Lobachevskian geometry but it cannot hold in Riemann's. Euclid assumes that there is exactly one parallel; Bolyai and Lobachevsky assume that there is more than one; but Riemann assumes that there is none.

However, Theorem 75 was proved without assuming any parallel postulate; therefore, some axiom or axioms of our system must be eliminated if we are to get a geometry without parallels. (See Figure 7.8.)

An analysis of the proof of Theorem 75 indicates that the contradiction comes from a line intersecting another in two distinct points. For this to be a contradiction two facts must hold: there must be two distinct points of intersection and it must be impossible for two lines to intersect in more than one point. The second condition is Theorem 4, which follows from the Axiom that two points determine a unique line; the first condition is assured by D and G being on opposite sides of line AB, which is assured by the plane separation theorem, which in turn is assured by Pasch's Axiom. One begins to see that the geometry of Riemann is a strange one indeed. It turns out that in the spherical geometry two lines intersect in two points and that it is true that every line separates the plane; in single elliptic, on the other hand, two lines intersect in exactly one point but no line separates the plane.

The Age of Hilbert

In the late nineteenth century a new approach, the beginning of critical examinations into the foundations of geometry came into being. This period also brought an interesting epilogue to the history of attempts to prove the Parallel Postulate.

It was discovered that a considerable amount of Euclidean geometry could be developed without the Postulate of Archimedes; that is, without an assumption of continuity. Saccheri and Lambert and all the others had made generous use of continuity assumptions in their arguments. Now, with the foundations of geometry undergoing intense investigation, it was discovered that if the Postulate of Archimedes is rejected the Fifth does not follow from the assumption that the sum of the angles of a triangle is equal to two right angles. In other words, there can exist a non-Archimedean geometry in which the sum of the angles of every triangle is equal to two right angles but where the Fifth does not hold.

This is a fitting climax to the chain of events started by the Parallel Postulate. Now, in every way, Euclid has been vindicated. Not only has the parallel postulate been shown to be independent of the others (we shall discuss its independence in the last chapter) but his form of it has been proved superior to the other form; those statements that were once regarded as equivalent to the Fifth have proved to be so only when propped up by the Postulate of Archimedes.

Hopefully, the reader is fully prepared to investigate a new and unfamiliar geometry. We might, however, make a final clarification. Strictly speaking, any geometry that is not "Euclidean" may be called "non-Euclidean." Thus the finite geometries introduced in the beginning of the text are "non-Euclidean" geometries. Any geometry denying *any* statement of Euclidean geometry may be called "non-Euclidean." It is customary, however, to restrict this title to those geometries that deny the parallel postulate.

EXERCISES 9.1

1. Check the references listed at the end of Part III to find examples of fallacious proofs of the Fifth that involve direction, infinite areas, or some assumption equivalent to the Fifth.

2. What is wrong with the following: Given a line *m* and a perpendicular to *m* from a point *A* not on it. Let it intersect *m* at a point *B*. Through *A* there exists exactly one line perpendicular to line *AB*. This line is parallel (non-intersecting) to *m*. Therefore, we have proved that through a point not on a given line there exists at most one line parallel to the given line. (Suggestion: compare this with exercise 1, Exercises 7.2.)

9.2   The Geometry of Bolyai-Lobachevsky

To study the geometry of Bolyai and Lobachevsky, often called *hyperbolic* geometry, all we will need is a new axiom, namely, any denial of some form of the Euclidean parallel postulate. The particular form we choose makes a difference in the development of the system.

Since the time of Proclus most geometers have taken "Playfair's Axiom" as their choice for a parallel postulate. If this is the statement chosen, the contradiction takes the following form:

Through a point not on a given line, more than one line can be drawn not intersecting the given line.

Indeed, this is the form used by Gauss, Bolyai, and Lobachevsky in beginning their studies of the new geometry.

Unfortunately, in order to begin in this manner, we are forced to introduce considerations of continuity. For it is known that there are two types of lines through a point not on a given line: those that intersect the given line and those that do not. It can be shown that there are an infinite number of each type. In the usual development it is then stated that the *first* of the nonintersecting lines are to be called the *parallels*— and that there are two such first, or limiting, lines. But to assume or to prove that such lines exist one must implicitly or explicitly introduce continuity considerations.

To avoid this we shall adopt an axiom first suggested by Hilbert. We have modified it to make it much stronger than need be and thereby to get to the heart of the subject matter more quickly.

Axiom 17 (*Hyperbolic Parallel Postulate, or HPP*). If P is any point not on a given line m, then there exist exactly two rays, say $\overrightarrow{PR}$ and $\overrightarrow{PS}$, which:

(a) *are not opposite rays*

(b) *do not intersect m*

(c) *are such that any ray, say $\overrightarrow{PQ}$, intersects m iff $\overrightarrow{PQ}$ is between $\overrightarrow{PR}$ and $\overrightarrow{PS}$.*

Definition 50. Each of the two rays whose existence is given in HPP is called a *parallel to m through P.*

Having introduced Axiom 17 it is now possible to prove some of the characteristic theorems of this new geometry. It should be kept in mind that every theorem proved in Chapters 5, 6, 7, and 8 will hold in the new geometry.

Axiom 17 tells us that any ray between the parallel rays to a line m must intersect m. A modification of this is presented as the first theorem in the new geometry.

Theorem 108. With any point P (not on a line m) as endpoint, if a ray lies between a ray parallel to m, and a ray intersecting m, then it intersects m.

Restatement: *If $\overrightarrow{PR}$ and $\overrightarrow{PS}$ are the parallels through P to a line m, and if B is any point on m, then any ray $\overrightarrow{PQ}$ falling between $\overrightarrow{PR}$ and $\overrightarrow{PB}$ intersects m.*

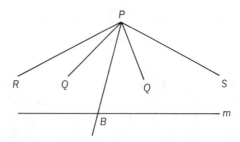

FIGURE 9.1

Proof: For if $\overrightarrow{PB}$ intersects m, then it follows from HPP that $\overrightarrow{PB}$ is between $\overrightarrow{PR}$ and $\overrightarrow{PS}$. If now $\overrightarrow{PQ}$ is a ray falling between $\overrightarrow{PR}$ and $\overrightarrow{PB}$, then it follows from Theorem 51a that $\overrightarrow{PQ}$ is between $\overrightarrow{PR}$ and $\overrightarrow{PS}$. Hence, from HPP it must intersect m.

Similarly, if ray $\overrightarrow{PQ}$ is between $\overrightarrow{PB}$ and $\overrightarrow{PS}$.   ●

It will soon become evident that there are many nonintersecting lines that are not parallels. The next theorem says, in effect, that a parallel is the "first" of the nonintersecting lines.

Theorem 109. If $\overrightarrow{PQ}$ does not intersect a line m, but every ray between $\overrightarrow{PQ}$ and $\overrightarrow{PB}$, where B is a point on m, does intersect m, then $\overrightarrow{PQ}$ is parallel to line m.

Proof: Let m be a line, P a point not on it, $\overrightarrow{PQ}$ a ray that does not intersect m. By HPP there exist two rays $\overrightarrow{PR}$ and $\overrightarrow{PS}$ through P and parallel to m. Let B be any point on m such that it is false that B, P, and Q are collinear. Then Q falls on one side or the other of line PB. It follows from HPP that $\overrightarrow{PR}$ and $\overrightarrow{PS}$ must be on opposite sides of line PB; suppose Q falls on the R side of $\overrightarrow{PB}$.

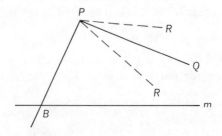

FIGURE 9.2

Now either $\overrightarrow{PR}$ is between $\overrightarrow{PB}$ and $\overrightarrow{PQ}$, $\overrightarrow{PQ}$ is between $\overrightarrow{PB}$ and $\overrightarrow{PR}$, or $\overrightarrow{PR} = \overrightarrow{PQ}$. (Why?)

By hypothesis, $\overrightarrow{PQ}$ does not intersect m; hence, it follows from Theorem 108 that it cannot lie between $\overrightarrow{PB}$ and $\overrightarrow{PR}$.

Also by hypothesis, every ray between $\overrightarrow{PQ}$ and $\overrightarrow{PB}$ intersects m; hence, by HPP, $\overrightarrow{PR}$ cannot lie between $\overrightarrow{PB}$ and $\overrightarrow{PQ}$.

It follows, therefore, that $\overrightarrow{PQ} = \overrightarrow{PR}$.

A similar argument holds if Q is on the S side of PB.   ●

It follows as an immediate corollary of HPP that any perpendicular from a point P to a line m must lie between the parallels through P to line m. We can now show:

Theorem 110. If Q is the foot of the perpendicular from a given point P to a given line m, and $\overrightarrow{PR}$ and $\overrightarrow{PS}$ are the parallels through P to m, then $\angle RPQ \cong \angle SPQ$.

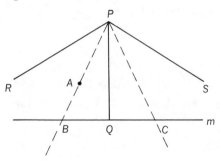

FIGURE 9.3

Proof: Suppose not. Then either $\angle SPQ < \angle RPQ$ or $\angle RPQ < \angle SPQ$. If $\angle SPQ < \angle RPQ$, then there exists a point A interior to $\angle RPQ$ such that $\angle APQ \cong \angle SPQ$ and, by Theorem 108, $\overrightarrow{PA}$ intersects m at a point B.

Now on m take C such that $B*Q*C$ and $B\text{-}Q \cong Q\text{-}C$ so that $\triangle BQP \cong \triangle CQP$ by SAS and therefore $\angle CPQ \cong \angle BPQ$. But $\angle APQ = \angle BPQ \cong \angle SPQ$. So by transitivity $\angle CPQ \cong \angle SPQ$, which implies that $\overrightarrow{PC}$ and $\overrightarrow{PS}$ are the same. (Why?)

But this is impossible because $\overrightarrow{PC}$ intersects m and $\overrightarrow{PS}$ does not. Hence, our assumption is false.

A similar argument eliminates $\angle RPQ < \angle SPQ$.

Hence, it follows that $\angle RPQ \cong \angle SPQ$.   ●

The converse of Theorem 110 is also true.

Theorem 111. If $\overrightarrow{PR}$ and $\overrightarrow{PS}$ are the parallels through P to a given line m, then the bisector of $\angle RPS$ is perpendicular to line m.

Proof: Given that $\overrightarrow{PA}$ is the bisector of $\angle RPS$, it follows that $\overrightarrow{PA}$ must intersect m (why?) at some point Q, and that $\angle RPQ \cong \angle SPQ$. Suppose that $\overrightarrow{PQ}$ is not perpendicular to m.

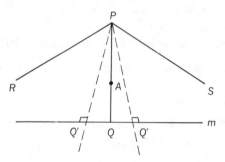

FIGURE 9.4

Then by Theorem 93 and Theorem 110 there exists a line PQ' through P and perpendicular to m, and such that $\angle RPQ' \cong \angle SPQ'$. Thus PQ' is also a bisector of $\angle RPS$, which contradicts Theorem 86.

It follows, therefore, that if $\overrightarrow{PA}$ is an angle bisector, it is also the perpendicular to m. ●

Although the diagrams have been drawn to indicate that the interior of the angle formed by parallel rays $\overrightarrow{PR}$ and $\overrightarrow{PS}$ contain m, this has not yet been established. Of course it would be quite embarrassing if false, for it would be almost painful to visualize condition (c) of Axiom 17 if the rays pointed upward. The next theorem assures us that the diagrams have not misled us. (See Figure 9.5.)

Theorem 112. If Q is the foot of the perpendicular from a point P to a given line m, and $\overrightarrow{PR}$ and $\overrightarrow{PS}$ are the parallels through P to m, then $\angle RPQ$ and $\angle SPQ$ are acute.

Proof: Suppose not. By Theorem 110 they must be congruent to each other. If they are both right angles, then $\overrightarrow{PR}$ and $\overrightarrow{PS}$ are opposite, contradicting HPP. If they are both obtuse, then $\overrightarrow{PE}$, the ray making a right angle with $\overrightarrow{PQ}$, would lie within $\angle SPQ$ or $\angle RPQ$ and hence by Theorem 108 would have to intersect m. By Theorem 78 this is impossible. The angles must, therefore, both be acute. ●

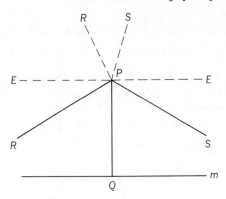

FIGURE 9.5

This theorem helps us to clarify a problem raised in Chapter 5. It was stated there that no angle analogue for Theorem 40 exists; that it cannot be proved that any line through an interior point of an angle, but not containing the vertex, cuts one of the sides. It should now be evident that to prove such a statement is, in effect, to prove the contradictory of Axiom 17. Therefore, it should be equally evident that to prove an analogue for Theorem 40 a Euclidean parallel postulate would be needed.

Using Theorem 112, it can now be proved that:

Theorem 113. If $\overrightarrow{PS}$ is a parallel through P to a line m, and N is a point of $\overrightarrow{PS}$ and X is any point such that $N*P*X$, then:

(a) It is false that $\overrightarrow{PX}$ is parallel to m
(b) It is false that $\overrightarrow{PX}$ intersects m
(c) Line PX ($= PS$) is nonintersecting with m.

Proof: Left as an exercise.

This theorem formally establishes some concepts that may have been intuitively evident; the theorem is not completely trivial, however. In this geometry that which is intuitively evident may be trivially true; on the other hand, it may be actually false. One must be careful of putting too much trust in one's intuition.

In keeping with this admonition, we shall carefully define some concepts whose meaning under other circumstances might very well have been left as part of the universal language.

Definition 51. Two noncollinear rays $\overrightarrow{PR}$ and $\overrightarrow{QS}$, where P and Q are distinct points, are said to be *in the same direction* iff they are on the same side of line PQ.

Definition 52. If $\overrightarrow{PS}$ is a parallel to m through P, and if $\overrightarrow{QX}$ is any ray on m, in the same direction as $\overrightarrow{PS}$, then $\overrightarrow{PS}$ is said to be *parallel to $\overrightarrow{QX}$*.

Let us carefully note the significance of Definition 52. Whereas HPP and Definition 50 tell us when a ray is parallel to a line, Definition 52 tells us when a ray is parallel to a ray. It tells us, for example, that while a ray may be parallel to a line, it is not parallel to *any* ray on that line. As

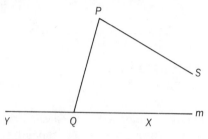

FIGURE 9.6

illustrated in Figure 9.6, $\overrightarrow{PS}$ is parallel to m, and to $\overrightarrow{QX}$; but, $\overrightarrow{PS}$ is not parallel to $\overrightarrow{QY}$.

It is still not possible for us to speak of two *lines* being parallel to each other. In fact, because of the way in which parallels have been introduced, we have yet to answer the following question: if a ray is parallel through a point P to a line m, must it follow that at any other point on the line containing the ray there exists another ray on the line and parallel to m? The answer to this question is supplied by the next theorem.

Theorem 114. Let m be a line, P a point not on m, $\overrightarrow{PR}$ a parallel to m through P; if A is any point on the line containing $\overrightarrow{PR}$, that is, if *either* $P*A*R$, *or* $A*P*R$, then $\overrightarrow{AR}$ is parallel to m.

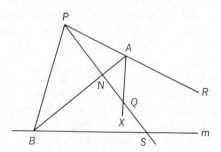

FIGURE 9.7

Proof:
  Case 1. Let A be any point such that $P*A*R$; let B be any point on m; let X be any point interior to $\angle BAR$; and, let Q be any point on $\overrightarrow{AX}$ on the R side of m.

  Now Q is interior to $\angle BAR$ (why?); it is also interior to $\angle BPR$. (Why?) It then follows, from Theorem 108 and Definition 18, that $\overrightarrow{PQ}$ intersects m in some point, say S. It is also the case that $\overrightarrow{PQ}$ intersects $B–A$ in a point N. (Why?) So from Pasch's axiom applied to $\triangle BNS$ it follows that $\overrightarrow{AQ} = \overrightarrow{AX}$ intersects $B–S$. (Why?)

  It was given that $\overrightarrow{AR}$ (as a subset of $\overrightarrow{PR}$) does not intersect line m. It has been shown that any ray $\overrightarrow{AX}$ interior to $\angle BAR$ intersects line m; therefore, by Theorem 109, $\overrightarrow{AR}$ is a parallel through P to line m.

  (Because R is an arbitrary point, and because we wished to keep the statement of the theorem from becoming any more complicated, we have ignored the case $P*R*A$. But to include this case would lead to no difficulty because there always exists a point R' on $\overrightarrow{PR}$ such that $P*A*R'$ and the proof proceeds as in Case 1—except that the conclusion would then read that $\overrightarrow{AR'}$ is parallel to m.)

  Case 2. Suppose now that A is a point such that $A*P*R$, B is any point on m, and X is any interior point of $\angle BAR$. Then there exists a point Q on

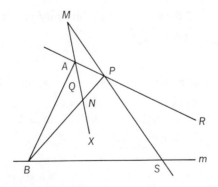

FIGURE 9.8

$\overrightarrow{AX}$ such that Q is on the A side of m, and the A side of line BP. (Why?)

  Let M be a point such that $Q*A*M$. Then $\overrightarrow{MP}$ intersects line m in some point, say S. (Why?)

  In $\triangle BAP$, $\overrightarrow{AQ}$ intersects $B–P$ in some point N; in $\triangle BPS$, $\overrightarrow{AQ} = \overrightarrow{AX}$ intersects $B–S$. (Why?)

From Theorem 113 it follows that $\overrightarrow{AR}$ (as a subset of line AR) does not intersect line m. It has been shown that any ray $\overrightarrow{AX}$ interior to $\angle BAR$ must intersect line m; therefore, by Theorem 109, $\overrightarrow{AR}$ is a parallel through A to line m.   ●

Once Theorems 113 and 114 have been proved it is possible to offer the following definition with the assurance that it is meaningful.

Definition 53. Given $\overrightarrow{PS}$ is a parallel to m and given X, Y are points on line PS, then $\overrightarrow{XY}$ is said to be *parallel to m in the same sense as* $\overrightarrow{PS}$ iff $\overrightarrow{XY}$ is not opposite $\overrightarrow{XS}$.

Language Rule 17. *If* $\overrightarrow{PS}$ *is parallel to m, then it is possible to speak of* LINE PS *being* PARALLEL TO m IN THE SAME SENSE; *if this language is used, however, one must then distinguish between line sense PS and line sense SP.*

We conclude this section by proving two theorems that show how parallels of this geometry are quite like those of Euclidean geometry and by proving one theorem that shows how different they are.

Although Definition 52 tells us under what circumstances $\overrightarrow{PS}$ can be said to be parallel to $\overrightarrow{QX}$, it does not guarantee that $\overrightarrow{QX}$ will be parallel to $\overrightarrow{PS}$. Theorem 115 fills this gap.

Theorem 115. Two rays are always mutually parallel.

Restatement: *If* $\overrightarrow{AR}$ *is a parallel to* $\overrightarrow{BS}$, *it is to be shown that* $\overrightarrow{BS}$ *is a parallel to* $\overrightarrow{AR}$.

Proof: From A drop a perpendicular to $\overrightarrow{BS}$ intersecting at a point C. We know that $\overrightarrow{CS}$ would have to be nonintersecting with $\overrightarrow{AR}$; to show that it is parallel we shall use Theorem 109. Thus, it is to be shown that any ray interior to $\angle ACS$ intersects $\overrightarrow{AR}$.

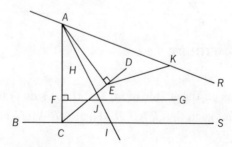

FIGURE 9.9

Let $\overrightarrow{CD}$ be a ray interior to $\angle ACS$, with D on the B side of $\overrightarrow{AR}$. Now from A let A-E be perpendicular to line CD; E must fall on $\overrightarrow{CD}$ because $\angle DCS$, $\angle ACD$ are acute angles and, therefore, E cannot coincide with C or be on the opposite side of AC without contradicting the exterior angle theorem. Hence, E lies interior to $\angle ACS$.

Therefore, $\angle ACE$ is an acute angle, and $\angle AEC$ is a right angle of $\triangle AEC$, so by Theorem 82 A-E < A-C.

Now on A-C there exists a point F such that A-$F \cong A$-E; let FG be perpendicular to A-C and on the same side of A-C as R and S.

E also lies interior to $\angle CAR$ (or else, $\overrightarrow{CE}$ meets $\overrightarrow{AR}$), so $\angle EAR < \angle FAR$. Let $\angle FAH \cong \angle EAR$. Then by Theorem 108 $\overrightarrow{AH}$ must meet $\overrightarrow{BS}$ in some point I. So in $\triangle ACI$, line FG must meet A-I in some point J.

On $\overrightarrow{AR}$ let K be a point such that A-$K \cong A$-J. Then $\triangle AFJ \cong \triangle AEK$ by SAS. So corresponding angles $\angle AFJ$, $\angle AEK$ are congruent. But $\angle AFJ$ is a right angle; therefore, $\angle AEK$ is a right angle. By construction, $\angle AED$ is a right angle, therefore, $\overrightarrow{ED} = \overrightarrow{EK}$ and $\overrightarrow{CE}$ intersects $\overrightarrow{AR}$ at K.

It follows from Theorem 109 that $\overrightarrow{CS}$ is parallel to $\overrightarrow{AR}$, and hence by Theorem 114 that $\overrightarrow{BS}$ is parallel to $\overrightarrow{AR}$.   ●

This theorem assures us that the parallel property for rays is a symmetric property. What about transitivity? Before one jumps to a conclusion on this question a look at HPP might be of value. Observe that while $\overrightarrow{PR}$ and $\overrightarrow{PS}$ are each parallel to m they are not parallel to each other. Thus if there is to be a transitivity property it must be restricted as in Theorem 116.

Theorem 116. If two rays are each parallel (in the same direction) to a third, then they are parallel to one another.

Proof: There are two cases to be considered: the case in which the two rays are on opposite sides of the third and the case in which they are on the same side of the third.

Case 1. Let $\overrightarrow{AR}$, $\overrightarrow{CT}$ both be parallel to $\overrightarrow{BS}$ on opposite sides of $\overrightarrow{BS}$. Then A-C must meet $\overrightarrow{BS}$ in a point D. (See Figure 9.10.)

Let $\overrightarrow{AE}$ be any ray through A between $\overrightarrow{AC}$ and $\overrightarrow{AR}$. Then by Theorem 108 this line will meet $\overrightarrow{BS}$ in a point, say F. Join C-F. Since $\overrightarrow{CT}$ is parallel to $\overrightarrow{BS}$, then by Theorem 115, $\overrightarrow{BS}$ is parallel to $\overrightarrow{CT}$, and by Theorem 114, $\overrightarrow{FS}$ is parallel to $\overrightarrow{CT}$. $\overrightarrow{FE}$ is interior to $\angle CFS$ (why?), so $\overrightarrow{FE} = \overrightarrow{AE}$ will meet $\overrightarrow{CT}$.

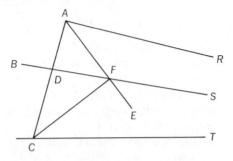

FIGURE 9.10

Since $\overrightarrow{AR}$ does not intersect $\overrightarrow{CT}$ (why?), but any line through A interior to $\angle CAR$ does, it follows from Theorem 109 that $\overrightarrow{AR}$ and $\overrightarrow{CT}$ are parallel.

Case 2. Suppose now that $\overrightarrow{AR}$ and $\overrightarrow{CT}$ are on the same side of $\overrightarrow{BS}$ and each is parallel to it. Then $\overrightarrow{AR}$ and $\overrightarrow{CT}$ cannot intersect. For if they did intersect, say in a point X, then through X there would exist two rays parallel (in the same direction) to a third. This is impossible. (Why?) Thus, they do not intersect, and either $\overrightarrow{AR}$ and $\overrightarrow{BS}$ are on opposite sides of $\overrightarrow{CT}$ or $\overrightarrow{CT}$ and $\overrightarrow{BS}$ are on opposite sides of $\overrightarrow{AR}$.

The proof is similar in either case; let us suppose the former, that is, that $\overrightarrow{AR}$ and $\overrightarrow{BS}$ are on opposite sides of $\overrightarrow{CT}$.

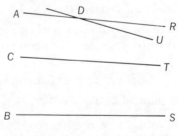

FIGURE 9.11

Suppose $\overrightarrow{AR}$ is not parallel to $\overrightarrow{CT}$. Then through any point D of $\overrightarrow{AR}$ there exists a ray $\overrightarrow{DU}$ parallel to $\overrightarrow{CT}$. It follows from Case 1 that $\overrightarrow{DU}$ is parallel to $\overrightarrow{BS}$. We already have that $\overrightarrow{AR}$ is parallel to $\overrightarrow{BS}$, so from Theorem 114 it follows that $\overrightarrow{DR}$ is parallel to $\overrightarrow{BS}$.

But from HPP, in the same direction, only one parallel to line BS can exist through a point D not on it. Therefore, $\overrightarrow{DU}$ must coincide with $\overrightarrow{DR}$ and thus $\overrightarrow{AR}$ is parallel to $\overrightarrow{CT}$. ●

We have now shown that if certain restrictions are made the parallels in this geometry have some of the properties of parallels in Euclidean geometry. It has also been shown that in this geometry there exists a distinction between "nonintersecting" lines and "parallel" lines; for, while all parallels are nonintersecting, it is not the case that all nonintersecting lines are parallels. Theorem 109, in effect, showed that parallels are the first of the nonintersecting lines. The next theorem (together with Theorem 77) establishes a more basic difference in their characteristics.

Theorem 117. Corresponding angles formed by two parallels and any transversal are not congruent.

Restatement: *Let $\overrightarrow{XR}$ and $\overrightarrow{YS}$ be parallel rays and line AB a transversal with A on $\overrightarrow{XR}$ and B on $\overrightarrow{YS}$; let C be a point such that $B*A*C$. It is to be proved that $\angle CAR$ is not congruent to $\angle CBS$.*

Proof: By Theorem 114 and Definition 52, $\overrightarrow{AR}$ and $\overrightarrow{BS}$ are parallel rays. Suppose now that $\angle CAR \cong \angle CBS$.

They cannot be right angles, for then $\angle BAR \cong \angle ABS$, contradicting Theorem 112.

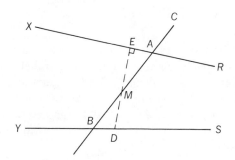

FIGURE 9.12

Let M be the midpoint of A–B and let the perpendicular from M to line AR intersect at a point E, which by the preceding statement is distinct from A. Whichever side of line AB point E falls on, take D on the opposite side of line AB such that B–$D \cong A$–E. It can then be shown that $\triangle MEA \cong \triangle MDB$ by SAS, and thus concluded that $\angle EMA \cong \angle DMB$.

Now since $\angle DMB$, $\angle DMC$ form a linear pair and $\angle EMA \cong \angle DMB$, then $\angle EMA$, and $\angle DMC$ are supplementary. (Why?) So by Theorem 62, Corollary 3, $\angle DMC$ and $\angle EMA$ form a linear pair; and, by Definitions 13 and 25, EMD is a (straight) line.

From the congruent triangles it follows that $\angle AEM \cong \angle MDB$; so, from Theorem 90 it follows that $\angle MDB$ is a right angle and by Definition 38 that $\angle MDS$ is a right angle.

It has now been shown that there exists a transversal ED of parallels $\overrightarrow{ER}$ and $\overrightarrow{DS}$ (using Theorem 114), such that $\angle RED$ and $\angle SDE$ are right angles. This contradicts Theorem 112.

Thus the assumption must be false and $\angle CAR$ and $\angle CBS$ are not congruent. ●

Corollary: *Alternate interior angles formed by two parallel lines and any transversal are not congruent.*

EXERCISES 9.2

1. Complete the proof of Theorems 110 and 111.
2. Prove Theorem 113.
3. Complete the proof of Theorem 114.
4. Complete the proof of Theorem 116.

9.3 A New Kind of Triangle

When two nonintersecting lines are met by a transversal the resulting figure is given no special name. When two parallel lines are met by a transversal, however, the resulting figure has some interesting properties and is sometimes called a *limit triangle* or an *asymptotic triangle*. Each of these names is descriptive in its own way but is also rather suggestive. So we shall merely call it a T-V-T (two-vertices-triangle). The following definition makes this more precise.

Definition 54. Given: any two parallel rays $\overrightarrow{XR}$ and $\overrightarrow{YS}$ met by a transversal m, at points A and B with $X*A*R$ and $Y*B*S$:

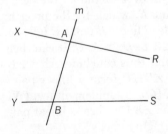

FIGURE 9.13

(a) The union of $\overrightarrow{AR}$, $\overrightarrow{BS}$, A, B and A–B is called a *T-V-T*.

(b) The segment A–B is called the *side* of the T-V-T.

(c) The angles $\angle BAR$ and $\angle ABS$ are called the *angles* of the T-V-T; also the *interior angles*.

(d) A, B are called the *vertices*.

(e) The angles $\angle XAB$, $\angle YBA$ and their respective vertical angles are called *exterior* angles of the T-V-T.

(f) An interior angle and an exterior angle of a T-V-T that are not adjacent are called *opposite interior* and *opposite exterior* angles relative to one another.

(g) The *interior* of a T-V-T is the intersection of:

   (i)   The R side of line AB
   (ii) The B side of line AR
   (iii) The A side of line BS

(h) The *exterior* of a T-V-T is the set of all points which are neither on the T-V-T nor in its interior.

Notation Rule 19. *A T-V-T with rays $\overrightarrow{AR}$ and $\overrightarrow{BS}$ joined by segment A–B will be denoted by:*

$$RABS$$

The figure has some of the properties of any ordinary triangle as shown by the following theorems.

Theorem 118. If a line passes through a point P interior to a T-V-T $RABS$, then:

(a) a line through P and either vertex intersects the other ray;

(b) a line through P and parallel to either ray intersects the side.

Proof:

Case a. Suppose that P lies interior to $RABS$. Then $\overrightarrow{AP}$ must intersect $\overrightarrow{BS}$ in some point C and, similarly, $\overrightarrow{BP}$ must intersect $\overrightarrow{AR}$; in each case this follows from Theorem 108.

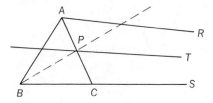

FIGURE 9.14

Case b. Suppose P lies interior to $RABS$ and $\overrightarrow{PT}$ is a ray parallel to either $\overrightarrow{AR}$ or $\overrightarrow{BS}$. Since $\overrightarrow{PT}$ intersects A–C at P and is parallel to $\overrightarrow{BS}$, then by Pasch's axiom it must intersect A–B. ●

Theorem 119. If a line not through a vertex of a T-V-T:

(a) intersects either ray, then it intersects the other ray, or the side;
(b) intersects the side, and is not parallel to either ray, then it intersects one of the two rays.

Proof:

Case a. If line m intersects a ray, say $\overrightarrow{AR}$ of $RABS$ at C, and does not go through a vertex, then m is not the same line as line BC. Therefore, there

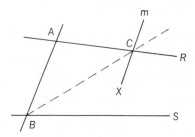

FIGURE 9.15

exists a point X which is interior to $RABS$ and either on the R side of BC or on the A side of BC. (Why does such a point exist?)

If it is on the R side, then it lies in $\angle BCR$ and so, by Theorems 108 and 114, it must intersect $\overrightarrow{BS}$. If it is on the A side of line BC, then in $\triangle ACB$, m intersects A–B, by Theorem 39.

Case b. If m intersects A–B at some point, say C, and is not parallel to either ray, then let $\overrightarrow{CT}$ be such a parallel. Then $RACT$ and $TCBS$ are T-V-T triangles. Line m has a point X either in $\angle ACT$ or $\angle BCT$ (but not

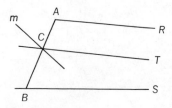

FIGURE 9.16

both). Therefore, by Theorem 118, m intersects either $\overrightarrow{AR}$ or $\overrightarrow{BS}$ (but not both). ●

From the time of the creation of this geometry to the present it has sometimes served man's intuition to think of parallel lines as meeting at some fictitious point, let us call it an *ideal* point. If we now pause momentarily to put the preceding two theorems into this framework, it can be seen that the first theorem becomes an extension of Theorem 39 and the second of Pasch's axiom, where the ideal point serves as the third vertex.

The following two theorems are also similar to those for ordinary triangles.

Theorem 120. An interior angle of a T-V-T is less than the opposite exterior angle.

Proof: Let $RABS$ be a T-V-T, C a point such that $B*A*C$, so that $\angle CAR$ is an exterior angle. It is to be proved that $\angle CBS < \angle CAR$. A similar argument would work for the other interior angle.

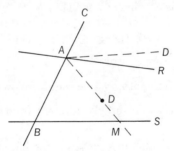

FIGURE 9.17

Through A, on the R side of line CB, let $\overrightarrow{AD}$ be such that $\angle CAD \cong \angle CBS$. Then D is on the C side of $\overrightarrow{AR}$, lies on $\overrightarrow{AR}$, or is on the B side of $\overrightarrow{AR}$.

If D is on the B side of $\overrightarrow{AR}$, then by Theorem 108 $\overrightarrow{AD}$ intersects $\overrightarrow{BS}$ at some point M and thus forms a triangle $\triangle ABM$ in which an interior angle $\angle ABM$ is congruent to an opposite exterior angle $\angle CAM$, contradicting Theorem 79. Hence, D cannot be on the B side of $\overrightarrow{AR}$.

By Theorem 117, it cannot lie on $\overrightarrow{AR}$.

Hence, D must lie on the C side of $\overrightarrow{AR}$, from which, by Definition 29, it follows that $\angle CBS < \angle CAR$. ●

Theorem 121. If in two T-V-T triangles, an angle of one is congruent to an angle of the other, and the sides are congruent, then the remaining angles are congruent.

Restatement: *Given two* T-V-T *triangles RABS and R'A'B'S', in which ∠B ≅ ∠B', and A–B ≅ A'–B', prove that ∠A ≅ ∠A'.*

Proof: Suppose that ∠A' < ∠A. Then there exists a point C such that ∠BAC ≅ ∠B'A'R', and C is interior to ∠BAR; hence, by Theorem 108, $\overrightarrow{AC}$ intersects $\overrightarrow{BS}$ at some point D.

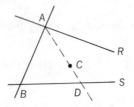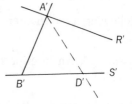

FIGURE 9.18

On $\overrightarrow{B'S'}$ there exists a point D' such that B–D ≅ B'–D'. Then by *SAS*, △ABD ≅ A'B'D', and ∠BAD ≅ ∠B'A'D'. But ∠BAD ≅ ∠B'A'R'; hence, by transitivity, ∠B'A'D' ≅ ∠B'A'R', which contradicts Axiom 14 (why?).

Similarly, if ∠A < ∠A'.

Therefore, by the Trichotomy theorem it follows that ∠A ≅ ∠A'. ●

The next theorem is astonishingly different from anything in Euclidean geometry.

Theorem 122. If in two T-V-T triangles the angles of one are congruent to the angles of the other, then the sides are congruent.

Proof: Given that ∠A ≅ ∠A', ∠B ≅ ∠B', it is to be shown that A–B ≅ A'–B' in the two T-V-T triangles RABS and R'A'B'S'.

Suppose A'–B' < A–B. Then there exists a point C on A–B such that B–C ≅ B'–A', and through C there exists a parallel, say $\overrightarrow{CT}$, to $\overrightarrow{AR}$ and hence, by Theorem 116, to $\overrightarrow{BS}$.

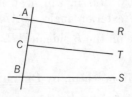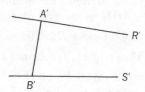

FIGURE 9.19

By Theorem 121 $\angle BCT \cong \angle A'$; but, since $\angle A' \cong \angle A$, it follows that $\angle A \cong \angle BCT$, which contradicts Theorem 117 (as well as Theorem 120). Hence, our assumption is false.

Similarly, if $A-B < A'-B'$.

So, by the Trichotomy for Segments theorem, $A-B \cong A'-B'$. ●

EXERCISES 9.3

1. Prove that in a T-V-T $RABS$, the bisector of each of the two angles intersects in a point interior to $RABS$.

2. A T-V-T is called *isosceles* if its two *angles* are congruent. Prove that if the sides of two isosceles T-V-Ts are congruent, then the angles of each are congruent to the angles of the other.

3. Prove that the perpendicular bisector of the side $A-B$ of an isosceles T-V-T $RABS$ is parallel to the rays $\overrightarrow{AR}$ and $\overrightarrow{BS}$.

4. Prove that if $\overrightarrow{CT}$ is the perpendicular bisector of $A-B$ in isosceles T-V-T $RABS$, then the perpendiculars from any point on $\overrightarrow{CT}$ to $\overrightarrow{AR}$ and $\overrightarrow{BS}$ are congruent.

5. Prove that if the perpendicular bisector $\overrightarrow{CT}$ of $A-B$ in $RABS$ is parallel to $\overrightarrow{AR}$ and $\overrightarrow{BS}$, then $RABS$ is isosceles.

10 New Shapes

Even when an author treats his subject as comprehensively as possible, he must use a certain amount of selectivity to keep the book from becoming unwieldy. Since it is not our aim to be comprehensive, a great deal of material must be left out or slighted. One should not assume that the deleted material is less important than that which is included.

If the subject matter is unadaptable or extraneous to the development of the text, there is no problem. However, many of the topics that might have been discussed in this chapter fall into the category of borderline cases both as to adaptability and relevance. In such a case the choice of materials to be included or deleted is arbitrary. It would have been possible, for example, to discuss the concept of *corresponding points*, which have as a locus the curve called a *horocycle* or the *equidistant* curve. We also might have examined *equivalent polygons* and their relevance to the *measurement of area*.

We have chosen to consider topics that are more obviously relevant to the development of the rest of the text and that easily generate interesting and instructive exercises. But the reader is encouraged to pursue additional topics on his own; many stimulating ones will be found in the references listed at the end of Part III.

10.1 Absolute Geometry

In Chapter 2 of this text we presented and discussed three axiom systems: 1, 2, and 3. It will be remembered that Axiom Sets 1 and 2 differed in only one axiom. In Axiom Set 1 there was a Euclidean parallel axiom; in Axiom Set 2 there was an axiom which said that no nonintersecting lines exist. It should be recognized that this situation is comparable to the relationship between Euclidean and hyperbolic geometry. For here, too, both systems have the same set of axioms except for one; but in this case the denial of the Euclidean parallel axiom takes the form of asserting the existence of more than one parallel rather than saying that there are none. The comparison carries further.

Axiom Set 3 was created by taking the set of all axioms common to the other two. Thus it was evident that all of the theorems derived from this set must of necessity hold in both of the other systems. In fact, Axiom System 3 was a *part* of each of the other systems; the same theorems would have resulted if we had worked in either of the other systems and merely refrained from ever using Axiom 5 in a proof. A completely analogous situation holds in the relationship between Euclidean geometry and hyperbolic geometry.

The founders of hyperbolic geometry were aware of this common core of subject matter. Bolyai, in particular, was very much interested in the theorems common to the new geometry and Euclidean geometry, and gave them a name. He called this system of axioms and theorems *absolute* geometry.

The reader should now be able to appreciate why, in developing the material of Chapters 5, 6, 7, and 8, no use was made of a parallel postulate. It was excluded to make the material available in Chapters 9 and 10.

As stated in Section 8.5, there was no need to stop at Theorem 107. There is literally no end to the number of theorems that could have been proved. Those theorems that would be needed were proved and those for which there was no immediate need were not proved. On the same basis we must now introduce several more theorems of absolute geometry.

Theorem 123. A point is interior to a convex quadrilateral iff it lies between: two points on opposite sides; two points on adjacent sides; a vertex and a point on a side not having that vertex as endpoint; opposite vertices.

Proof: Left as an exercise.

Theorem 124. The segment between points on opposite sides of a convex quadrilateral must intersect the segment between points on the other two opposite sides.

Proof: Left as an exercise.

Theorem 125. In a convex quadrilateral the (rays containing the) diagonals lie interior to the angles with which they have a common vertex.

Proof: Left as an exercise.

Theorem 126. (a) The line joining points on opposite sides of a convex quadrilateral "divides" it into two convex quadrilaterals.

(b) A diagonal of a convex quadrilateral "divides" it into two triangles.

Proof: Left as an exercise.

Theorem 127. If *ABCD* is any convex quadrilateral with right angles at ∠*A* and ∠*B*, and *E* is a point such that *A*E*B*, then any line perpendicular to line *AB* at *E* must intersect segment *C–D*.

Proof: Left as an exercise.

Theorem 128. If *ABCD* is any convex quadrilateral with right angles at ∠*A* and ∠*B*, and *E* is any point such that *C*E*D*, then the line which passes through *E* and which is perpendicular to line *AB* intersects segment *A–B*.

Proof: Left as an exercise.

EXERCISES 10.1

1. Prove Theorem 123.
2. Prove Theorem 124.
3. Prove Theorem 125.
*4. Prove Theorem 126a.
*5. Prove Theorem 126b.
6. Prove Theorem 127.
7. Prove Theorem 128.

10.2   New Quadrilaterals

In this section we shall introduce two figures briefly mentioned in the section on history. Both Saccheri and Lambert introduced quadrilaterals from which they attempted to prove the Parallel Postulate. It will be remembered that before claiming a tenuous victory, each had derived a great many theorems from his hypothesis of the acute angle.

Since we have already introduced the HPP we shall be approaching the material from a different perspective. This in no way detracts from the fascination of these figures. The Saccheri quadrilateral, in particular, we find to be one of the most interesting figures in geometry. We trust that before long the reader will agree.

Definition 55. A convex quadrilateral $ABCD$ in which $\angle A$ and $\angle B$ are right angles and A–$D \cong B$–C is called a *Saccheri Quadrilateral*. A–B is

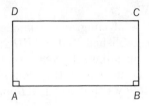

FIGURE 10.1

called the *base*. D–C is called the *summit*. Angles $\angle D$ and $\angle C$ are called the *summit angles*.

Notation Rule 20. *The quadrilateral defined in Definition 55 will be denoted by:*

$$\text{S.Q. } ABCD$$

where the first two letters of the quadrilateral named always represent the right angles.

According to the definition, any quadrilateral with two right angles and congruent *sides* qualifies as a Saccheri Quadrilateral. Therefore, as far as the definition is concerned, it is possible to refer to a square or a rectangle as a Saccheri Quadrilateral. This is true if we remain in absolute geometry, as we do in the next four theorems.

Theorem 129. If a line passes through the midpoints of the base and summit of a S.Q., then it is perpendicular to both of them.

Proof: Given a S.Q. $ABCD$ with points E, F, such that $A*E*B$, $D*F*C$, and A–$E \cong E$–B, D–$F \cong F$–C, it is to be shown that $EF \perp AB$ and $EF \perp DC$.

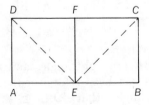

FIGURE 10.2

It follows immediately from the definition of S.Q. and from what is given that $\triangle DAE \cong \triangle CBE$. Hence, $\angle AED \cong \angle BEC$ and $D\text{–}E \cong C\text{–}E$. $\triangle DFE \cong \triangle CFE$ by *SSS*. Hence, $\angle DFE \cong \angle CFE$ and, therefore, by definition, are right angles.

It must be the case that $\overrightarrow{ED}$ is between $\overrightarrow{EA}$ and $\overrightarrow{EF}$, and that $\overrightarrow{EC}$ is between $\overrightarrow{EB}$ and $\overrightarrow{EF}$. (Why?)

By corresponding parts of congruent triangles, $\angle DEF \cong \angle CEF$, and since we have already established that $\angle AED \cong \angle BEC$, it follows from Theorem 64 on addition of adjacent angles, that $\angle AEF \cong \angle BEF$. Since by definition they form a linear pair, they must be right angles.

By definition it now follows that $EF \perp AB$ and $EF \perp DC$. ●

Corollary: *The lines containing the base and summit of a S.Q. are nonintersecting and nonparallel lines.*
Proof: Follows from Theorems 129, 78, and 117.

Theorem 130. If a line is the perpendicular bisector of the base of a S. Q. it is also the perpendicular bisector of the summit.

Proof: Given a S.Q. $ABCD$ with a point E such that $A*E*B$ and $A\text{–}E \cong E\text{–}B$, it is to be shown that there exists a point F such that $D*F*C$, such that the perpendicular bisector of $A\text{–}B$ passes through F and such that $EF \perp DC$ and $D\text{–}F \cong F\text{–}C$.

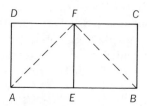

FIGURE 10.3

It follows from Theorem 127 that there exists a point F such that $D*F*C$ and such that the perpendicular bisector of $A\text{–}B$ passes through F. $\triangle AEF \cong \triangle BEF$ by *SAS*. Hence $A\text{–}F \cong B\text{–}F$, $\angle EAF \cong \angle EBF$.

It must be the case that $\overrightarrow{AF}$ is between $\overrightarrow{AD}$ and $\overrightarrow{AE}$ and that $\overrightarrow{BF}$ is between $\overrightarrow{BE}$ and $\overrightarrow{BC}$. (Why?)

By definition, $\angle A$, $\angle B$ are right angles and thus $\angle A \cong \angle B$. It then follows (from what has just been established) from Theorem 65 on the subtraction of adjacent angles, that $\angle DAF \cong \angle CBF$. Since $D\text{–}A \cong C\text{–}B$, it follows by *SAS* that $\triangle DAF \cong \triangle CBF$ and thus that $D\text{–}F \cong F\text{–}C$.

But now, by Theorem 64 (Addition), it follows that $\angle DFE \cong \angle CFE$ and, since they form a linear pair, that they are right angles. So by definition $EF \perp DC$.

Therefore, by definition, EF is the perpendicular bisector of D–C. ●

Theorem 131. The perpendicular bisector of the summit of a S.Q. is also the perpendicular bisector of the base.

Proof: Left as an exercise. (Hint: prove by contradiction.)

Theorem 132. The summit angles of a S.Q. are congruent.

Proof: Left as an exercise.

If we ignore the Corollary to Theorem 129, which requires a hyperbolic theorem and definition in its proof, it will be seen that the proofs of these theorems use only the theorems from absolute geometry; each of them is true for squares and rectangles.

It is not often, however, that squares and rectangles are called Saccheri Quadrilaterals. This is because of the characteristic properties the latter have in hyperbolic geometry. This is brought out sharply in the next theorem.

In studying the proof of this fundamental theorem it should not pass unnoticed how much of the preceding development of this text is required for its solution.

Theorem 133. The summit angles of a S.Q. are acute.

Proof: In S.Q. $ABCD$, let E be a point such that $D*C*E$, and let F be a point such that $A*B*F$.

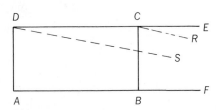

FIGURE 10.4

Let $\overrightarrow{DS}$ be parallel to $\overrightarrow{AB}$ and let $\overrightarrow{CR}$ be parallel to $\overrightarrow{BF}$, then $\overrightarrow{DS}$ and $\overrightarrow{CR}$ are both parallel to $\overrightarrow{AB}$ and to each other. (Why?)

By the Corollary to Theorem 129, the base and summit of a S.Q. are nonparallel and nonintersecting; hence, it follows that $\overrightarrow{DS}$ is between $\overrightarrow{DA}$ and $\overrightarrow{DC}$ and that $\overrightarrow{CR}$ is between $\overrightarrow{CB}$ and $\overrightarrow{CE}$. (Why?)

Now from Theorem 121 it follows that in the two T-V-T triangles $SDAF$ and $RCBF$, $\angle SDA \cong \angle RCB$. Furthermore, from Theorem 120 it follows that in T-V-T $RCDS$, $\angle CDS < \angle ECR$. Hence, using Theorem 104 and Definitions 46 through 49, it follows that $\angle CDA < \angle ECB$.

According to Theorem 132 $\angle CDA \cong \angle DCB$; therefore, from Theorem 67 (Presubstitution) it follows that $\angle DCB < \angle ECB$.

Because $\angle DCB$, $\angle ECB$ form a linear pair they are supplementary. Because $\angle DCB < \angle ECB$ they are not right angles. Therefore, using Definition 38, Theorems 89b, 89a, and 88, it follows that $\angle DCB$ is acute.

Thus, it follows that $\angle CDA$ is acute. (Why?) ●

This theorem has a traumatic effect on one's intuition. It is one thing to agree that there can exist two parallels to a given line through a given point; one can almost do this abstractly. When this is accepted, one still has to cope with the idea that the parallel rays "point downward"; if they are to be nonintersecting, intuition would have them "pointing upward." This is strange, but one can adjust to it. Now, however, something new enters the discussion.

We have never examined the properties of the lines in this system. We know that "line" is an undefined term; by the axioms assumed, especially the *betweenness* axioms, it is plausible to regard them as "straight" lines. This has been done in all of the figures presented up to this point, and if we had not entered the realm of hyperbolic geometry no question would have been raised. But what now?

Observe that the sides of a Saccheri Quadrilateral are congruent; it has now been shown that the summit angles are acute. How then does one draw the summit? Notice (in Figure 10.5) that if one draws the summit

FIGURE 10.5

straight, the angles do not look acute; if one draws the angles acute, the summit does not look straight.

The next figure introduced will hardly improve matters. It is fortunate, indeed, that diagrams are not required for proofs. They might be quite misleading in hyperbolic geometry.

Definition 56. A quadrilateral containing three right angles is called a *Lambert Quadrilateral*.

Notation Rule 21. *The quadrilateral' defined in Definition 56 will be denoted by:*

$$\text{L.Q. } ABCD$$

where the first three letters of the quadrilateral named will always represent the right angles.

As far as the definition is concerned it would be possible to refer to a square or a rectangle as a Lambert Quadrilateral. Once again it should be pointed out that in Euclidean geometry this is seldom done and, as the next theorem shows, in Hyperbolic geometry it cannot be done.

Theorem 134. In a L.Q. the fourth angle is acute.

Proof: Let $ABCD$ be a L.Q. with right angles at A, B, and C. Let E be a point such that $A*B*E$, and let F be a point such that $D*C*F$. Finally, let $B\text{–}A \cong B\text{–}E$ and $C\text{–}D \cong C\text{–}F$.

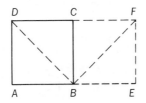

FIGURE 10.6

$\triangle DCB \cong \triangle FCB$ by SAS and thus their corresponding angles are congruent, as well as sides $D\text{–}B$ and $B\text{–}F$.

From Theorem 125 it follows that $\overrightarrow{BD}$ is between $\overrightarrow{BA}$ and $\overrightarrow{BC}$; it is also the case that $\overrightarrow{BF}$ is between $\overrightarrow{BC}$ and $\overrightarrow{BE}$.

It now follows that $\angle DBA \cong \angle FBE$ (why?); so $\triangle DBA \cong \triangle FBE$ by SAS, $\angle A \cong \angle E$, and $D\text{–}A \cong F\text{–}E$.

It was given that $\angle A$ is a right angle; it has been shown that $\angle A \cong \angle E$. Therefore, $\angle A$ and $\angle E$ are right angles.

By definition, it is now the case that quadrilateral $AEFD$ is a S.Q. and so by Theorem 133 $\angle ADC$ is acute. ●

It is now possible to prove the converse of Theorem 129; contrary to one's first impression, this is not a theorem from absolute geometry.

Theorem 135. If a line is perpendicular to both the base and summit of a S.Q., it joins the midpoints.

Proof: Left as an exercise (Hint: This statement is equivalent to "the line joining the midpoint of the base and summit of a S.Q. is the only line perpendicular to both of them" when used in conjunction with Theorems 129 and 134.)

The following theorem and its converse are very useful. It should be noted that they are about *any* convex quadrilaterals that have two right angles (and satisfy the other conditions).

Theorem 136. If, in a convex quadrilateral $ABCD$, the angles at A and B are right angles, and if A–$D < B$–C, then $\angle C < \angle D$.

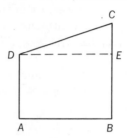

FIGURE 10.7

Proof: Since A–$D < B$–C, there exists a point E such that $B*E*C$ and A–$D \cong B$–E; but then quadrilateral $ABED$ is a S.Q., and from Theorem 132

$$\text{(a)} \quad \angle ADE \cong \angle BED$$

From the exterior angle theorem it follows that

$$\text{(b)} \quad \angle BCD < \angle BED$$

and from the definition of *less than*, that

$$\text{(c)} \quad \angle ADE < \angle ADC$$

Now, from Theorem 67 (Pre-Substitution) and lines (a) and (c), we have

$$\text{(d)} \quad \angle BED < \angle ADC$$

and from (b) and (d) together with Theorem 69 (Transitivity), it can be concluded that

$$\angle BCD < \angle ADC, \text{ that is, } \angle C < \angle D. \quad \bullet$$

Theorem 137. If, in a convex quadrilateral $ABCD$, the angles at A and at B are right angles, and if $\angle C < \angle D$, then A–$D < B$–C.

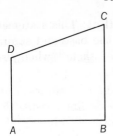

FIGURE 10.8

Proof: Suppose that A–$D \cong B$–C. Then, by definition, $ABCD$ is a S.Q., and the assumption that $\angle C < \angle D$ contradicts Theorem 132.

Suppose B–$C < A$–D. Then, by Theorem 136, $\angle D < \angle C$, and this contradicts our hypothesis (by Theorem 66, the Trichotomy Theorem for angles).

Thus, by Theorem 57, the Trichotomy Theorem for segments, it is the case that A–$D < B$–C. ●

Theorem 138. In any convex quadrilateral $ABCD$, if $\angle A$ and $\angle B$ are right angles, and $\angle C \cong \angle D$, then the figure is a S.Q.

Proof: Left as an exercise.

EXERCISES 10.2

1. If a perpendicular is erected *at* any point *on* the side of a S.Q. it must intersect the opposite side. Answer true or false. If true, prove it; if false, give a counterexample.

2. If a perpendicular is erected *at* any point *on* the summit of a S.Q. it must intersect the base. Answer true or false. If true, prove it; if false, give a counterexample.

3. If a perpendicular is *dropped from* a point on a side of a S.Q. *to* the opposite side line, it must intersect the side. Answer true or false. If true, prove it; if false give, a counterexample.

4. Prove Theorem 131.

5. Prove Theorem 132.

6. Complete the proof of Theorem 133.

7. Prove Theorem 135.

8. Prove Theorem 138.

9. Prove that in a L. Q. the sides adjacent to the acute angle are greater than their respective opposite sides.

10. Prove that in a S.Q. the summit is greater than the base.

11. Prove that the diagonals of a S.Q. are congruent.

12. Prove that the diagonals of a S.Q. do not bisect each other.

13. Prove that the perpendicular bisector of the base of a S.Q. passe through the intersection of the diagonals.

14. Prove that if from the extremities of one side of a triangle, line are drawn perpendicular to the line passing through the midpoints of th other two sides, a S.Q. is formed.

15. Prove that the perpendicular bisector of any side of a triangle i perpendicular to the line joining the midpoints of the other two side

*16. Prove that a line through the midpoint of one side of a triangle an perpendicular to the line that bisects a second side at right angles bisect the third side.

17. Prove that the line joining the midpoints of the equal sides of : S.Q. is perpendicular to the line joining the midpoints of the base an summit; prove that it bisects the diagonals.

18. Prove that the line joining the midpoints of the equal sides of . S.Q. does not pass through the intersection of the diagonals.

10.3   Congruent Quadrilaterals

Notation Rule 22: By $ABCD \leftrightarrow EFGH$ we shall mean:

$A \leftrightarrow E$	$\angle A \leftrightarrow \angle E$	$A\text{–}B \leftrightarrow E\text{–}F$
$B \leftrightarrow F$	$\angle B \leftrightarrow \angle F$	$B\text{–}C \leftrightarrow F\text{–}G$
$C \leftrightarrow G$	$\angle C \leftrightarrow \angle G$	$C\text{–}D \leftrightarrow G\text{–}H$
$D \leftrightarrow H$	$\angle D \leftrightarrow \angle H$	$A\text{–}D \leftrightarrow E\text{–}H$

Definition 57. Given any two quadrilaterals $ABCD$, $EFGH$, if ther exists at least one correspondence $ABCD \leftrightarrow WXYZ$, where $W, X, Y,$ ؛ are E, F, G, H in some order such that

$\angle A \cong \angle W$	$A\text{–}B \cong W\text{–}X$
$\angle B \cong \angle X$	$B\text{–}C \cong X\text{–}Y$
$\angle C \cong \angle Y$	$C\text{–}D \cong Y\text{–}Z$
$\angle D \cong \angle Z$	$A\text{–}D \cong W\text{–}Z$

then this correspondence is called a *congruent correspondence* or a *con gruence*. The two quadrilaterals are called *congruent*.

Notation Rule 23: *If $ABCD \leftrightarrow EFGH$ is a congruent correspondenc for quadrilaterals $ABCD$ and $EFGH$, this will be denoted by:*

$$ABCD \cong EFGH$$

Some of the techniques used to prove the following theorems are quite different from those used to prove most elementary congruence theorems n Euclidean geometry.

Theorem 139. If in L.Q.'s *ABCD* and *EFGH*, *ABCD* ↔ *EFGH*, ∠*D* ≅ ∠*H* and, if any *one* of the following holds:

(a) *A–D* ≅ *E–H*   or   (b) *D–C* ≅ *H–G*

r

(c) *A–B* ≅ *E–F*   or   (d)̇ *B–C* ≅ *F–G*

then, *ABCD* ≅ *EFGH*.

Proof: The proofs of (a) and (b) are similar, as are the proofs of (c) and (d) but, as we shall see, the proofs of (a) and (c) are quite different.

Case (a). By hypothesis *A–D* ≅ *E–H*. Suppose *D–C* < *H–G*. Then there exists a point *I* such that *H*I*G* and *D–C* ≅ *H–I*; △*ADC* ≅ △*EHI* by *SAS*.

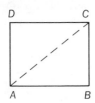

FIGURE 10.9

At *I* drop a perpendicular to line *EF* intersecting at a point *J* such that *E*J*F* (follows from Theorem 128).

Now, $\overrightarrow{AC}$ is between $\overrightarrow{AD}$ and $\overrightarrow{AB}$; also $\overrightarrow{EI}$ is between $\overrightarrow{EH}$ and $\overrightarrow{EJ}$. (Why?) Therefore, △*ABC* ≅ △*EJI*. (Why?)

Now ∠*DCA* ≅ ∠*HIE*, ∠*ACB* ≅ ∠*EIJ*; therefore, ∠*DCB* ≅ ∠*HIJ*. Since ∠*C* is a right angle, so is ∠*HIJ*, and hence so is ∠*JIG*. By construction, so is ∠*IJF*. Therefore, quadrilateral *IJFG* has four right angles, contradicting Theorem 134.

A similar argument holds if *H–G* < *D–C*. Therefore, from the Trichotomy Theorem it follows that *D–C* ≅ *H–G*.

It now follows that △*ADC* ≅ △*EHG*; then, since $\overrightarrow{EG}$ is between $\overrightarrow{EH}$ and $\overrightarrow{EF}$, it follows by *ASA* (or *SAA*) that △*ABC* ≅ △*EFG*. Thus, *ABCD* ≅ *EFGH*.

Case (c). By hypothesis, *A–B* ≅ *E–F*. Let *H'* be a point such that *D*A*H'* and *A–H'* ≅ *E–H*. Then △*BAH'* ≅ △*FEH* (why?), and *H'–B* ≅ *H–F*.

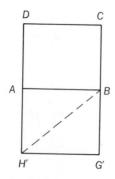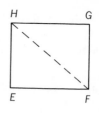

FIGURE 10.10

Let G' be a point such that $C*B*G'$ and $B\text{–}G' \cong F\text{–}G$. Join G', H'. Now $\overrightarrow{BH'}$ is between $\overrightarrow{BA}$ and $\overrightarrow{BG'}$ (why?) and $\overrightarrow{FH}$ is between $\overrightarrow{FE}$ and $\overrightarrow{FG}$. Thus $\triangle BG'H' \cong \triangle FGH$. (Why?)

It now follows that $\angle AH'G' \cong \angle EHG$ and $ABG'H' \cong EFGH$. Therefore, by transitivity $\angle H' \cong \angle D$. Also $\angle G'$ and $\angle C$ are right angles. So by Theorem 138, $G'CDH'$ is a S.Q.

By definition of S.Q., $D\text{–}C \cong H'\text{–}G'$. By Theorem 135, $B\text{–}C \cong B\text{–}G'$ and $D\text{–}A \cong A\text{–}H'$. Hence, by transitivity and definition, $ABCD \cong EFGH$. ●

There are many ways to attempt the above proof, and because a Lambert Quadrilateral is actually being constructed, one must be wary not to assume what is being proved.

This theorem, once proved, provides an easy test for congruence of Lambert Quadrilaterals that can be used in the following proof about Saccheri Quadrilaterals:

Theorem 140. If in S.Q.'s $ABCD$ and $EFGH$, $ABCD \leftrightarrow EFGH$, $\angle D \cong \angle H$ and, if any *one* of the following holds:

    (a) $C\text{–}D \cong G\text{–}H$ *or*   (b) $A\text{–}B \cong E\text{–}F$ *or*   (c) $B\text{–}C \cong F\text{–}G$

then $ABCD \cong EFGH$.

Proof:

    Case (a). By hypothesis, $C\text{–}D \cong G\text{–}H$, $\angle D \cong \angle H$.

    Suppose $H\text{–}E < D\text{–}A$. Then there exists a point I such that $D*I*A$ and $D\text{–}I \cong H\text{–}E$. Then $\triangle DIC \cong \triangle HEG$.

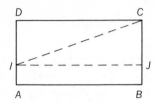 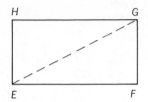

FIGURE 10.11

On $\overrightarrow{CB}$, let $C\text{-}J \cong G\text{-}F$. Then $\overrightarrow{CI}$ is between $\overrightarrow{CJ}$ and $\overrightarrow{CD}$. (Why?) Hence, $\triangle ICJ \cong \triangle EGF$. (Why?)

It now follows that $C*J*B$. (Why?)

Since it can be shown that $\angle DIJ$ and $\angle IJC$ are right angles, it follows that $\angle AIJ$ and $\angle BJI$ are right angles. This contradicts Theorem 134.

Similarly, if $D\text{-}A < H\text{-}E$. Therefore, $H\text{-}E \cong D\text{-}A$.

From this, it can be shown that $\triangle ADC \cong \triangle EHG$ and $\triangle ACB \cong \triangle EGF$, and thus finally that $ABCD \cong EFGH$.

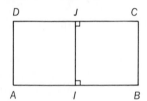 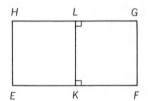

FIGURE 10.12

Case (b). This follows from constructing the perpendiculars at the midpoints of $A\text{-}B$ and $E\text{-}F$ and using Theorem 139, case (c).

Case (c). Follows as in Case (b) from Theorem 139, Case (b). ●

EXERCISES 10.3

1. Fill in the proofs of Theorems 139 and 140, Case (a).
2. Complete the proof of Theorem 140, Case (b).
3. Complete the proof of Theorem 140, Case (c).
4. If $ABCD$ and $EFGH$ are two L.Q.'s with acute angles at D and H, prove that:

(a) If $A\text{-}B \cong E\text{-}F$ and $B\text{-}C \cong F\text{-}G$, then $ABCD \cong EFGH$.

(b) If $D\text{-}A \cong H\text{-}E$ and $A\text{-}B \cong E\text{-}F$, then $ABCD \cong EFGH$.

(c) If $D\text{-}A \cong H\text{-}E$ and $B\text{-}C \cong F\text{-}G$, then $ABCD \cong EFGH$.

*(d) If $D\text{-}A \cong H\text{-}E$ and $D\text{-}C \cong H\text{-}G$, then $ABCD \cong EFGH$.

5. If $ABCD$ and $EFGH$ are S.Q.'s with acute angles at C, D, G, and H, prove that:

(a) If $A-B \cong E-F$ and if $B-C \cong F-G$, then $ABCD \cong EFGH$.

(b) If $A-B \cong E-F$ and if $C-D \cong G-H$, then $ABCD \cong EFGH$.

(c) If $B-C \cong F-G$ and if $C-D \cong G-H$, then $ABCD \cong EFGH$.

10.4   A Comparison of Hyperbolic and Euclidean Properties

In this section we will briefly survey some of the properties of hyperbolic geometry that contrast most strikingly with Euclidean properties. There will be no attempt to present this material formally. Some properties will be introduced by means of theorems, others will merely be mentioned or briefly discussed.

Parallels

In Definitions 51 and 52 we stated that in order for two rays to be parallel they must be *in the same direction,* and it was stated what that meant. Let us now refer to that direction as the *direction of parallelism.*

By now the reader must have anticipated the next theorem. It says, in effect, that parallel lines (rays) converge in the direction of parallelism.

Theorem 141. If $\overrightarrow{PR}$ and $\overrightarrow{QS}$ are any two parallel rays, and A, B, are points such that $P*A*B*R$, let C, D be the points where the perpendiculars from A and B to line QS intersect QS, then $B-D < A-C$.

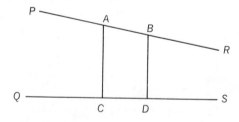

FIGURE 10.13

Proof: Because $\overrightarrow{PR}$ is parallel to $\overrightarrow{QS}$, so is $\overrightarrow{AR}$ and $\overrightarrow{BR}$. Then $\angle CAR$ and $\angle DBR$ are each acute angles.

But since $A*B*R$, it follows that $\angle DBA$, $\angle DBR$ form a linear pair and, hence, that $\angle DBA$ is obtuse.

Then in (convex?) quadrilateral $CDBA$ $\angle C$, $\angle D$ are right angles and $\angle CAB < \angle DBA$. So, by Theorem 137, $B\text{-}D < A\text{-}C$. ●

It should be immediately apparent from the proof of this theorem that if X is any point such that $A*B*X$, and Y is the foot of the perpendicular from X to line QS, then $X\text{-}Y < B\text{-}D$. This says that any segment "farther out" in the direction of parallelism is less than the preceding ones. But this does not imply that parallels become less than any length no matter how small; that is, that the distance between parallels converges to zero; or, that the lines are asymptotic. The next theorem, in effect, says just that.

Theorem 142. Let $X\text{-}Y$ be any segment whatsoever; then there exists a segment $W\text{-}Z$ such that W is on $\overrightarrow{PR}$, a parallel to QS, and $W\text{-}Z$ is a perpendicular to QS, and $W\text{-}Z < X\text{-}Y$.

Proof: Let $\overrightarrow{PR}$ and $\overrightarrow{QS}$ be parallel and PA perpendicular to QS. Let $X\text{-}Y$ be any segment whatsoever; then, if $P\text{-}A < X\text{-}Y$ we are through. If $P\text{-}A \cong X\text{-}Y$ then this theorem follows from Theorem 141. Suppose then, that $X\text{-}Y < P\text{-}A$.

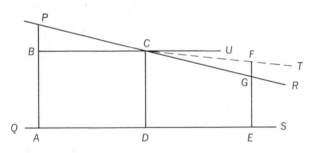

FIGURE 10.14

Let B be a point such that $A*B*P$ and $A\text{-}B \cong X\text{-}Y$. Through B let $\overrightarrow{BU}$ be perpendicular to PA and in the direction $\overrightarrow{QS}$. Then, by Theorem 119, $\overrightarrow{BU}$ intersects $\overrightarrow{PR}$ at some point, say C. Let CD be the perpendicular from C to QS.

Then $\angle RCD < \angle BCD$. (Why?) So let $\overrightarrow{CT}$ be such that $\angle BCD \cong \angle TCD$; then $\angle RCD < \angle TCD$.

Let E be a point such that $A*D*E$ and $A\text{-}D \cong D\text{-}E$, and let F be a point on $\overrightarrow{CT}$ such that $B\text{-}C \cong C\text{-}F$.

Now it can be shown that $F\text{-}E \cong A\text{-}B$, and FE is perpendicular to QS

(left as an exercise). Furthermore, $\overrightarrow{PC}$ must intersect $F-E$ at some point, say G. (Why?)

Thus $E-G < E-F$; $E-F \cong A-B$; $A-B \cong X-Y$. So $E-G < X-Y$, where G is a point on $\overrightarrow{PR}$ and EG is perpendicular to $\overrightarrow{QS}$. Hence $E-G$ is the segment $W-Z$. This completes the proof. ●

It should be apparent also that parallel rays diverge in the opposite direction and become larger than any given segment. This could be proved now, but we leave this as an exercise and turn to other interesting implications of the theory of parallels.

While discussing the historical development of non-Euclidean geometries, we stated that in the new geometry there exists an *absolute unit* of length. A rigorous discussion of this concept lies beyond the synthetic approach, but the following intuitive explanation may help to clarify it.

Given points A, Y, P, and X, such that $A*Y*P*X$; and given parallels $\overrightarrow{AR}$, $\overrightarrow{YS}$, $\overrightarrow{PT}$, and $\overrightarrow{XU}$, it follows immediately from Theorem 120 that $\angle AXU < \angle APT < \angle AYS$. (See Figure 10.15.)

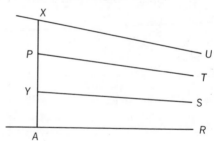

FIGURE 10.15

Furthermore, given two T-V-T's $RABS$ and $R'CDS'$, such that $\angle B$ and $\angle D$ are right angles, then it follows immediately from Theorem 121 that if $A-B \cong C-D$, then $\angle A \cong \angle C$; and from Theorem 122 it follows that if $\angle A \cong \angle C$, then $A-B \cong C-D$. (See Figure 10.16.)

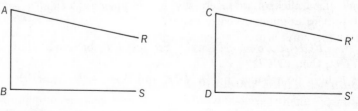

FIGURE 10.16

The following definition will make it easier to discuss this:

Definition 58. Given $\overrightarrow{PR}$ a parallel to m through P, and Q the intersection point of the perpendicular from P to m, then $\angle QPR$ is called *the angle of parallelism for P–Q.*

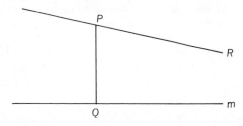

FIGURE 10.17

We can now say that the angles of parallelism corresponding to equal distances are equal, and conversely. Furthermore, as the distances become greater, the angle of parallelism becomes smaller, and as the distances become smaller, the angles of parallelism become larger. There is a functional relationship between the measure of the angle of parallelism $\angle QPR$ and the length of the segment P–Q; furthermore, to every acute angle there corresponds a distance for which the angle is the angle of parallelism.

In both Euclidean and hyperbolic geometries there is an absolute standard to which all angles can be compared, the right angle. No one needs to keep a right angle hidden in a vault at the Bureau of Standards to preserve it, for it can always be reconstructed. Thus, there exists a natural *unit* of measure (some given fractional part of a right angle) that could be reconstructed if it were ever lost. This is what is meant by saying that angles have an *absolute* unit of measure in both geometries.

In Euclidean geometry there is no absolute standard for units of length; they are quite arbitrary. However, once it has been determined in hyperbolic geometry that to every angle there corresponds a definite segment, namely the segment associated with that angle when it is regarded as an angle of parallelism, an interesting new property comes into being. From the unit of angular measure one can determine a corresponding unit of linear measure, a unit having a structural connection with the geometry and thus one that is an absolute unit of length.

Nonintersecting Nonparallel Lines

It has already been shown that if two lines have a common perpendicular they are nonintersecting and nonparallel. A proof, originated by

Hilbert, establishes the converse and occurs in most texts on hyperbolic geometry. Because the proof is long and complicated and does not introduce any new techniques that make its reproduction here worthwhile, we shall omit it and merely state the theorem.

Theorem 143. If two straight lines neither intersect nor are parallel, they must have a common perpendicular.

This is an *existence* theorem (in fact, Hilbert's proof actually shows how to construct such a line if one knows how to construct parallels). The *uniqueness* of the common perpendicular was established in effect in the proof of Theorem 134.

A property more interesting than the existence of a common perpendicular to two nonintersecting lines is:

Theorem 144. Let the common perpendicular to two nonintersecting lines m, n, meet at P, Q. Let A, B be points such that $P*A*B$ and let perpendiculars through A, B to n meet at C, D respectively, then

$$P\text{–}Q < A\text{–}C, \; A\text{–}C < B\text{–}D$$

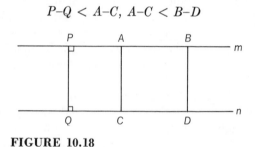

FIGURE 10.18

Proof: $PQCA$ is a L.Q. Hence, $\angle CAP$ is acute and, therefore, $P\text{–}Q < A\text{–}C$ by Theorem 137.

Because $\angle CAP$ is acute, $\angle CAB$ is obtuse. Since quadrilateral $PQDB$ is a L.Q., $\angle DBP$ is acute. But $\angle DBP = \angle DBA$. Hence, in (convex?) quadrilateral $CDBA$, $\angle DBA < \angle CAB$.

Therefore, $A\text{–}C < B\text{–}D$ by Theorem 137.

A similar argument holds if the points are on the opposite sides of line PQ. ●

This theorem, in effect, shows that nonintersecting nonparallel lines diverge as the distance from the common parallel increases. It can also be shown that the distance apart becomes greater than any arbitrarily chosen segment. Thus, it would seem that nonintersecting lines are as shown in Figure 10.19.

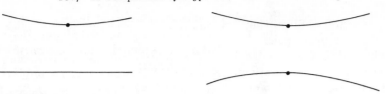

FIGURE 10.19

Triangles

As previously stated, there are many interesting concepts in hyper-bolic geometry that one might pursue in discussing triangles. We have chosen to omit discussions of area and defects of triangles, but several properties occur in this geometry which, although not well suited to the synthetic approach, should not be ignored. Accordingly, the remainder of the theorems will illustrate these properties.

Definition 59. Any *three* angles $\angle A$, $\angle B$, and $\angle C$ are said to be *taken together less than two right angles*, iff:

(a) $m(\angle X) + m(\angle Y) = m(\angle Z)$ exists, where $\angle X$, $\angle Y$ are any two of the three angles; and

(b) $\angle V$ and $\angle W$ are two angles taken together less than two right angles, where $\angle V$ is some angle of the set $m(\angle Z)$ and $\angle W$ is the remaining one of the three angles.

Theorem 145. The three angles of every right triangle are taken together less than two right angles.

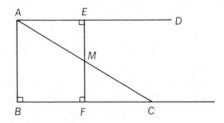

FIGURE 10.20

Proof: Let ABC be any triangle with a right angle at B. At A, on the opposite side of line AC from B, let $\angle CAD \cong \angle BCA$. Let M be the midpoint of $A\text{-}C$, and lines ME and MF the perpendiculars from M to AD and BC, respectively.

Then $\triangle FCM \cong \triangle EAM$ by SAA and, therefore, $\angle AME \cong \angle CMF$. But $\angle CMF$, $\angle FMA$ form a linear pair; therefore, $\angle AME$, $\angle FMA$ are supplementary. Since they are adjacent, by Theorem 62, Corollary 3, they form a linear pair.

Thus, $BFEA$ is a quadrilateral with right angles at B, F, and E. Hence, its fourth angle is acute. But $m(\angle BAE) = m(\angle BAC) + m(\angle BCA)$.

Therefore, $\angle B$, $\angle A$, and $\angle C$ of triangle ABC are taken together less than two right angles. •

Theorem 146. The three angles of *any* triangle are taken together less than two right angles.

Proof: Let ABC be any triangle. By Theorem 91, at least two of its angles are acute, say A and B.

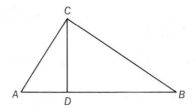

FIGURE 10.21

Then a line through C perpendicular to AB must intersect A–B at some point D. (Why?)

Therefore, C–D divides triangle ABC into two right triangles ADC and BDC.

From the preceding theorem, $m(\angle DAC) + m(\angle ACD) = m(\angle M)$ and $m(\angle M) < m(\angle X)$ where X is any right angle.

And $m(\angle DBC) + m(\angle DCB) = m(\angle N)$, and $m(\angle N) < m(\angle X)$.

Therefore, $\angle M$ and $\angle N$ are taken together less than two right angles. •

These results, strange as they are, could have been anticipated from the discussion of the history of attempts to prove the Fifth. For if the statement:

The sum of the angles of any triangle equals two right angles.

is equivalent to the Parallel Postulate, then when one statement is denied so is the other. Of course, whether the sum was to be less than or greater than two right angles still had to be determined.

The last of the properties to be discussed in this section may also have been anticipated—a clue was given by Theorem 122, where the congruence of the angles of two *T-V-T* triangles implied the congruence of the sides. The property is introduced below as statement (S). Unfortunately, it cannot be introduced as a theorem because the proof does not lend itself to the synthetic method. In such a proof we would be required to say that:

The sum of four angles (of a quadrilateral) is less than 360 degrees (four right angles).

There is no easy way, in the synthetic approach, to express a statement equivalent to this. The problem is not only to find a definition but to find a definition that is usable.

If such a definition were available, then the proof of the following statement would be relatively easy.

(S) If two triangles ABC and DEF are such that $ABC \leftrightarrow DEF$, $\angle A \cong \angle D$, $\angle B \cong \angle E$, $\angle C \cong \angle F$, then $\triangle ABC \cong \triangle DEF$.

This statement introduces one of the most astounding properties of hyperbolic geometry. In effect, it says that there is no such thing as two figures being similar but not congruent. Thus, for a photograph to resemble its subject it would have to be a lifesize photograph: moreover, all the fields that depend upon similarity and proportion would be drastically altered. Consider what would happen to painting, designing, drafting, and architecture. Consider what would happen to the world around us. It would be a very strange new world.

Yet such a world is a possible one. The last chapter will explain how it might even be that this geometry most closely describes the space world around us.

EXERCISES 10.4

1. In the proof of Theorem 142:

(a) prove that $\overrightarrow{CT}$ is between $\overrightarrow{CU}$ and $\overrightarrow{CR}$;
(b) prove that $E\text{–}F \cong B\text{–}A$, and $\angle DEF$ is a right angle.

2. Complete the proof of Theorem 146.

3. Prove that parallel rays diverge in the direction opposite to the direction of parallelism.

4. Try to define what it means to say that the sum of four angles is less than (or equal to) four right angles.

5. Assuming one has the definition of exercise 4, prove statement (S) of the text.

Which of the following statements are true in *both* Euclidean and hyperbolic geometry. Explain.

6. There exist equilateral quadrilaterals.

7. There exist parallelograms.

8. Two lines are parallel if they have no points in common.

9. If two lines are perpendicular to the same line, then they are parallel.

10. The perpendicular to a given line from a point not on it is unique.

11. The exterior angle of a triangle is greater than the opposite interior angle.

12. Given a line and a point not on the line, there exists at least one line which passes through the given point and is parallel to the given line.

13. If two sides of a triangle are not congruent, then the angles opposite them are not congruent and the greater angle is opposite the longer side.

14. The opposite sides of a parallelogram are equal.

15. All straight angles are equal to two right angles.

16. Given two lines and a transversal, if a pair of corresponding angles are congruent, then a pair of alternate interior angles are congruent.

17. If a S.Q. *ABCD* has right angles at *A* and *B*, then the angles at *C* and *D* are congruent to each other.

18. All squares have four equal angles.

19. The Pythagorean Theorem holds.

11 A Model World

From the list of theorems in the last two chapters, one may choose numerous denials of the Euclidean parallel axiom and its equivalent forms:

1. Through a point outside a given line, more than one parallel to the given line exists.
2. If two lines are cut by a transversal such that the interior angles on the same side of the transversal are, taken together, less than two right angles, the lines do not necessarily meet on that side.
3. Parallel lines are not everywhere equidistant.
4. The sum of the angles of any triangle is less than two right angles.

These are only a few. Each denies some statement of Euclidean geometry; but the statements on the list are consistent with each other. Or so we are told.

How do we know? How do we know that neither Saccheri nor Lambert actually reached a contradiction? How do we know that the system of Bolyai-Lobachevsky is free from contradictions, that no theorem derived contradicts another, and that no such theorems will ever be found?

It is often said that Bolyai and Lobachevsky proved the independence of the parallel postulate but this is not quite accurate. It was not until some years later that a model was found for their system. Perhaps the first to do so was E. Beltrami (1835–1900). Another model, the one we shall discuss, was presented by H. Poincaré (1854–1912) in his work *Science and Hypothesis*. Both of these models are often credited to Klein, who discussed them in relation to projective geometry.

11.1   A Model

We shall now return to the Euclidean plane and assume the full extent of its properties. The purpose is to construct a model for hyperbolic geometry from a part of that plane.

Consider a circle, which will be called the *fundamental circle*. A Euclidean point will be considered a point in this model if and only if it is interior to the fundamental circle. Points on the circle are to be "points at infinity."

Consider now a circle that cuts the fundamental circle orthogonally; that is, in such a manner that the tangents to each circle at the points of intersection are perpendicular to each other. By a "straight line" we shall mean that *part* of such a circle that is interior to the fundamental circle.

By various techniques of modern Euclidean geometry, many interesting properties of such "lines" can be derived. For example, it can be shown that through two points interior to the fundamental circle, exactly one circle exists that is orthogonal to the fundamental circle; and, that two circles orthogonal to the fundamental circle can intersect in at most one point interior to the fundamental circle.

Furthermore, a distance function can be defined in such a way that the distance between any interior point and points nearer and nearer to the fundamental circle grows larger without bound. Thus this model, in effect, may be regarded as infinite in extent.

In such a model it is actually easy to "see" some of the properties that seemed so strange and were impossible to diagram in a strictly Euclidean framework.

Figure 11.1 shows two parallels PR and PS through a point P not on a line m. It indicates the angle θ that these two lines make with each other.

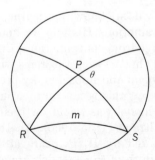

FIGURE 11.1

Figure 11.2 shows a T-V-T $RABS$, in which $R = S$ (a point at infinity). It also shows an ordinary triangle ABD in which the sum of the angles are apparently less than two right angles.

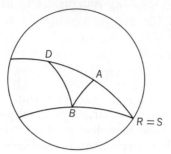

FIGURE 11.2

Figure 11.3 shows a S.Q. $ABCD$ with right angles at A and at $B;$ and a L.Q. $BADE$ with right angles at B, A, and D.

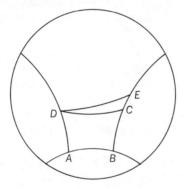

FIGURE 11.3

What makes this model so valuable is not so much that it is easy to diagram the results but that all the properties of hyperbolic geometry can be rigorously established in it; that it can easily be generalized to three dimensions by taking a fundamental sphere and spheres orthogonal to it; and, finally, that all of these results are actually being obtained in Euclidean geometry. The model exists in the Euclidean plane (or space) although it is a model for hyperbolic geometry.

The model, therefore, establishes a relative test for the consistency of hyperbolic geometry. That is, hyperbolic geometry is as consistent as Euclidean geometry; a contradiction could arise only if it already existed in the Euclidean model. It is a matter of fact that over the centuries no one has found an inconsistency in Euclidean geometry; therefore, it is very likely that there is none. This is not a very satisfactory test for consistency but it is the best one we have. But whether or not there exists an absolute test for the consistency of Euclidean geometry is irrelevant to our purposes. The main result of the model is that it shows that hyperbolic geometry is on as firm a logical base as Euclidean geometry; furthermore, it shows once and for all that the Parallel Postulate of Euclidean geometry is independent of the others.

However, the existence of the model also raises new questions. For, if they are both shown to be consistent, how does one decide which is the "true" geometry? Which geometry better describes the space world around us?

11.2   A Model World

Imagine a world which is a large sphere with the property that the temperature changes from point to point within the sphere. As one approaches the center of this sphere the temperature becomes hot and as one approaches the boundary of the sphere the temperature becomes very cold, approaching absolute zero. Furthermore, suppose that all material objects (including the inhabitants of this world) are extremely sensitive to changes in temperature and change instantaneously in size with each change in temperature in such a manner that they grow larger or indefinitely smaller as the temperature increases or decreases, respectively.

To an inhabitant of such a world it would seem to be of infinite extent, for as he approached the boundary of his world he would become smaller and smaller. To reach the boundary would require an infinite number of steps, and he would be as sure that his world was infinite in extent as we seem to be in regard to ours. There would be no way for him to become aware of his situation because any yardstick he carried with him would change in the same proportion.

It can be shown rigorously (using the calculus of variations) that for an inhabitant of such a world the shortest distance between two points would be along the arc of a circle that cuts the bounding sphere orthogonally. This is plausible also, for as he walked from one point to another and if he followed a path which swerved toward the center, his steps would be longer there; thus this path would give a smaller number of steps.

Imagine yet another fact about this world, namely, that light travels along the "shortest paths" along the arcs of circles orthogonal to the bounding sphere. Then, if a man walked toward an object following the shortest path, these shortest paths would actually look straight to him.

What would some of the other properties of this world be? The angle θ shown in Figure 11.1 might very well be visible to the inhabitants. But this angle can be shown to decrease as the point P and line m approach the center of the bounding sphere. Or, to put it another way, if the point P and line m are at a given distance from the center of the sphere, the angle θ decreases indefinitely as the radius of the bounding sphere increases. Thus, the angle θ may be made very small indeed.

Suppose now that Earth is at the center of such a sphere and that the radius of the sphere is so large that the angle θ is smaller than any instrument of man can detect. *In such a situation, the physical world around us would differ in no respect from that to which we are accustomed. But the geometry of Lobachevsky would apply to this world as legitimately as the geometry of Euclid.*

This, then, creates a paradox. If θ is non-existent, we are living in a Euclidean world; if θ exists, no matter how small, we are living in a Lobachevskian world. But how can we ever know that the angle θ is not so small that it remains undetectable even though present? How can we know which geometry is the one that actually describes the world around us?

11.3 Is Euclidean Geometry True?

Modern physics suggests that our world is more likely to be a non-Euclidean one than a Euclidean one, although the particular geometry that physicists have adopted is a modification of Riemann's geometry rather than that of Lobachevsky. But this is not what we want to stress here.

As far as mathematics is concerned, the question as to which geometry is the true one is not merely totally irrelevant but meaningless. As Poincaré says, to ask which is true is like asking which form of measurement is more correct, centimeters or inches? Is the polar coordinate system the "true" one or is it the rectangular system? These are meaningless questions.

This is not to suggest that mathematics need not keep in touch with reality, for almost everyone would agree that a mathematics divorced from reality would soon become sterile. But this is quite different from being concerned with "truth." Rather let us ask which geometry is the most convenient. To this there is a simple answer: Euclidean geometry is the simplest and most convenient to use and shall probably always be used in elementary applications.

This does not mean, however, that no practical value can be found in studying other geometries. All of the geometries, finite and infinite, Euclidean and non-Euclidean, are worthy of investigation. This is so even if our prime objective is to obtain the "truest" geometry, the geometry with the widest range of applications. For the history of mathematics teaches us that some of the most useful results in mathematics have often come from pursuits having no apparent "useful" purpose. We have seen an illustration of this in the unexpectedly rich results that poured forth when mathematicians attempted to answer a seemingly innocent question: can Euclid's Fifth postulate be proved from the others?

references

Bonola, Roberto. *Non-Euclidean Geometry*. Translated by H. S. Carslaw. Chicago: The Open Court Publishing Company, 1912. Reprinted by Dover Publications, Inc., 1955.

Carslaw, H. S. *Non-Euclidean Plane Geometry and Trigonometry*. New York: Longmans, Green and Company, 1916. Reprinted by Chelsea Publishing Company, 1960.

Kulczycki, Stepfan. *Non-Euclidean Geometry*. Translated by S. Knapowski. New York: Pergamon Press, 1961.

Lobachevsky, Nicholai. *Geometrical Researches on the Theory of Parallels*. Translated by G. B. Halsted. Chicago: The Open Court Publishing Company, 1914.

Moise, E. E. *Elementary Geometry from an Advanced Standpoint*. Reading, Massachusetts: Addison-Wesley Publishing Company, Inc., 1963.

Poincaré, Henri. *The Foundations of Science*. Translated by G. B. Halsted. New York and Garrison, New York: The Science Press, 1921.

Sommerville, D. M. Y. *The Elements of Non-Euclidean Geometry*. London: G. Bell and Sons, Ltd., 1914. Reprinted by Dover Publications, Inc., 1958.

Wolfe, Harold E. *Introduction to Non-Euclidean Geometry*. New York: Holt, Rinehart and Winston, Inc., 1945.

Young, J. W. *Lectures on Fundamental Concepts of Algebra and Geometry*. New York: The MacMillan Company, 1911.

appendix

Euclid's Axioms and

Common Notions and

the Statements of Book I

of the Elements[1]

The Definitions of Book I

1. A *point* is that which has no part.
2. A *line* is breadthless length.
3. The extremities of a line are points.
4. A *straight line* is a line which lies evenly with the points on itself.
5. A *surface* is that which has length and breadth only.
6. The extremities of a surface are lines.
7. A *plane surface* is a surface which lies evenly with the straight lines on itself.
8. A *plane angle* is the inclination to one another of two lines in a plane which meet one another and do not lie in a straight line.
9. And when the lines containing the angle are straight, the angle is called *rectilineal*.
10. When a straight line set up on a straight line makes the adjacent angles equal to one another, each of the equal angles is *right*, and the

[1] By permission of T. L. Heath, *The Thirteen Books of Euclid's Elements*, 3 vols., 2d ed. (New York: The Cambridge University Press, 1926. Reprinted by Dover Publications, Inc., 1956.)

straight line standing on the other is called a *perpendicular* to that on which it stands.

11. An *obtuse angle* is an angle greater than a right angle.
12. An *acute angle* is an angle less than a right angle.
13. A *boundary* is that which is an extremity of anything.
14. A *figure* is that which is contained by any boundary or boundaries.
15. A *circle* is a plane figure contained by one line such that all the straight lines falling upon it from one point among those lying within the figure are equal to one another.
16. And the point is called the *centre* of the circle.
17. A *diameter* of the circle is any straight line drawn through the centre and terminated in both directions by the circumference of the circle, and such a straight line also bisects the circle.
18. A *semicircle* is the figure contained by the diameter and the circumference cut off by it. And the centre of the semicircle is the same as that of the circle.
19. *Rectilineal figures* are those which are contained by straight lines, *trilateral* figures being those contained by three, *quadrilateral* those contained by four, and *multilateral* those contained by more than four straight lines.
20. Of trilateral figures, an *equilateral triangle* is that which has its three sides equal, an *isosceles triangle* that which has two of its sides alone equal, and a *scalene triangle* that which has its three sides unequal.
21. Further, of trilateral figures, a *right-angled triangle* is that which has a right angle, an *obtuse-angled triangle* that which has an obtuse angle, and an *acute-angled triangle* that which has its three angles acute.
22. Of quadrilateral figures, a *square* is that which is both equilateral and right-angled; an *oblong* that which is right-angled but not equilateral; a *rhombus* that which is equilateral but not right-angled; and a *rhomboid* that which has its opposite sides and angles equal to one another but is neither equilateral nor right-angled. And let quadrilaterals other than these be called *trapezia*.
23. *Parallel* straight lines are straight lines which, being in the same plane and being produced indefinitely in both directions, do not meet one another in either direction.

The Postulates

Let the following be postulated:
1. To draw a straight line from any point to any point.
2. To produce a finite straight line continuously in a straight line.

3. To describe a circle with any centre and distance.
4. That all right angles are equal to one another.
5. That, if a straight line falling on two straight lines make the interior angles on the same side less than two right angles, the two straight lines, if produced indefinitely, meet on that side on which are the angles less than the two right angles.

Common Notions

1. Things which are equal to the same thing are also equal to one another.
2. If equals be added to equals, the wholes are equal.
3. If equals be subtracted from equals, the remainders are equal.
4. Things which coincide with one another are equal to one another.
5. The whole is greater than the part.

The Forty-Eight Propositions of Book I

1. On a given finite straight line to construct an equilateral triangle.
2. To place at a given point (as an extremity) a straight line equal to a given straight line.
3. Given two unequal straight lines, to cut off from the greater a straight line equal to the less.
4. If two triangles have the two sides equal to two sides respectively, and have the angles contained by the equal straight lines equal, they will also have the base equal to the base, the triangle will be equal to the triangle, and the remaining angles will be equal to the remaining angles respectively, namely those which the equal sides subtend.
5. In isosceles triangles the angles at the base are equal to one another, and, if the equal straight lines be produced further, the angles under the base will be equal to one another.
6. If in a triangle two angles be equal to one another, the sides which subtend the equal angles will also be equal to one another.
7. Given two straight lines constructed on a straight line (from its extremities) and meeting in a point, there cannot be constructed on the same straight line (from its extremities), and on the same side of it, two other straight lines meeting in another point and equal to the former two respectively, namely each to that which has the same extremity with it.
8. If two triangles have the two sides equal to two sides respectively, and have also the base equal to the base, they will also have the angles equal which are contained by the equal straight lines.
9. To bisect a given rectilineal angle.

10. To bisect a given finite straight line.
11. To draw a straight line at right angles to a given straight line from a given point on it.
12. To a given infinite straight line, from a given point which is not on it, to draw a perpendicular straight line.
13. If a straight line set up on a straight line make angles, it will make either two right angles or angles equal to two right angles.
14. If with any straight line, and at a point on it, two straight lines not lying on the same side make the adjacent angles equal to two right angles, the two straight lines will be in a straight line with one another.
15. If two straight lines cut one another, they make the vertical angles equal to one another.
16. In any triangle, if one of the sides be produced, the exterior angle is greater than either of the interior and opposite angles.
17. In any triangle two angles taken together in any manner are less than two right angles.
18. In any triangle the greater side subtends the greater angle.
19. In any triangle the greater angle is subtended by the greater side.
20. In any triangle two sides taken together in any manner are greater than the remaining one.
21. If on one of the sides of a triangle, from its extremities, there be constructed two straight lines meeting within the triangle, the straight lines so constructed will be less than the remaining two sides of the triangle, but will contain a greater angle.
22. Out of three straight lines, which are equal to three given straight lines, to construct a triangle: thus it is necessary that two of the straight lines taken together in any manner should be greater than the remaining one.
23. On a given straight line and at a point on it to construct a rectilineal angle equal to a given rectilineal angle.
24. If two triangles have the two sides equal to two sides respectively, but have the one of the angles contained by the equal straight lines greater than the other, they will also have the base greater than the base.
25. If two triangles have the two sides equal to two sides respectively, but have the base greater than the base, they will also have the one of the angles contained by the equal straight lines greater than the other.
26. If two triangles have the two angles equal to two angles respectively, and one side equal to one side, namely, either the side adjoining the equal angles, or that subtending one of the equal angles, they will

also have the remaining sides equal to the remaining sides and the remaining angle to the remaining angle.

27. If a straight line falling on two straight lines make the alternate angles equal to one another, the straight lines will be parallel to one another.

28. If a straight line falling on two straight lines make the exterior angle equal to the interior and opposite angle on the same side, or the interior angles on the same side equal to two right angles, the straight lines will be parallel to one another.

29. A straight line falling on parallel straight lines makes the alternate angles equal to one another, the exterior angle equal to the interior and opposite angle, and the interior angles on the same side equal to two right angles.

30. Straight lines parallel to the same straight line are also parallel to one another.

31. Through a given point to draw a straight line parallel to a given straight line.

32. In any triangle, if one of the sides be produced, the exterior angle is equal to the two interior and opposite angles, and the three interior angles of the triangle are equal to two right angles.

33. The straight lines joining equal and parallel straight lines (at the extremities which are) in the same directions (respectively) are themselves also equal and parallel.

34. In parallelogrammic areas the opposite sides and angles are equal to one another, and the diameter bisects the areas.

35. Parallelograms which are on the same base and in the same parallels are equal to one another.

36. Parallelograms which are on equal bases and in the same parallels are equal to one another.

37. Triangles which are on the same base and in the same parallels are equal to one another.

38. Triangles which are on equal bases and in the same parallels are equal to one another.

39. Equal triangles which are on the same base and on the same side are also in the same parallels.

40. Equal triangles which are on equal bases and on the same side are also in the same parallels.

41. If a parallelogram have the same base with a triangle and be in the same parallels, the parallelogram is double of the triangle.

42. To construct, in a given rectilineal angle, a parallelogram equal to a given triangle.

43. In any parallelogram the complements of the parallelograms about the diameter are equal to one another.

44. To a given straight line to apply, in a given rectilineal angle, a parallelogram equal to a given triangle.

45. To construct, in a given rectilineal angle, a parallelogram equal to a given rectilineal figure.

46. On a given straight line to describe a square.

47. In right-angled triangles the square on the side subtending the right angle is equal to the squares on the sides containing the right angle.

48. If in a triangle the square on one of the sides be equal to the squares on the remaining two sides of the triangle, the angle contained by the remaining two sides of the triangle is right.

Index